Maths for the Mystified

An exploration of the history of mathematics and its relationship to modern-day science and computing

Dr Michael J de Smith

Maths for the Mystified

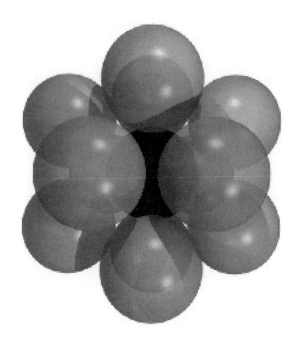

An exploration of the history of mathematics and its relationship to modern-day science and computing

510
SMI

Matador
9 De Montfort Mews
Leicester LE1 7FW, UK
Tel: (+44) 116 255 9311 / 9312
Email: books@troubador.co.uk
Web: www.troubador.co.uk/matador

www.mdesmith.com

To Christine

ISBN 10: 1 905237 81 2
ISBN 13: 978 1905237 81 4

Cover images: sections of the Mandelbrot set, generated by the author (see Section 13.2 for further information)
Page iii image "Kissing Numbers" © Wolfram Inc. (Mathworld)

MAR 1 4 2007

Cent

Typeset in 10pt Trebucht by Troubador Publishing Ltd, Leicester, UK
Printed in the UK by The Cromwell Press Ltd, Trowbridge, Wilts, UK

Matador is an imprint of Troubador Publishing Ltd

CONTENTS

ACKNOWLEDGEMENTS

This book has been developing as an idea in my mind for several years, and over that time many individuals have made observations that have found their way into the text. Pictures and text relating to various mathematicians have been prepared using the MacTutor website of the University of St Andrews, with their kind permission. Figure 3.2 is reproduced by permission of the Controller of Her Majesty's Stationery Office and the UK Hydrographic Office (www.ukho.gov.uk). Other images are acknowledged within the text where drawn from third party sources. I would like to thank all those who read and commented on the draft text, including my wife Christine, Sam, Joan, Derrick, my long-time software engineering colleague 'Harry' from Croatia, and finally, a special thanks to Rosemary Emanuel, an expert in education and mathematics, who both read and corrected various items of substance and style in the text. Any remaining errors, however, are solely the responsibility of the author!

PREFACE

The following is a true story...

Larry Walters, a delivery driver for a Hollywood film production company, had a boyhood dream to fly. As he sat in his backyard watching jets fly overhead he hatched his daring scheme. He purchased 45-50 weather balloons from an Army and Navy surplus store, tied most of them to a garden chair which he had tethered to his friend's car, and filled the balloons with helium gas. On June 2nd 1982 he strapped himself into the chair with some food, drinks, water containers to act as ballast and a pellet gun. He figured he would pop a few of the many balloons when it was time to descend.

Larry's plan was to cut the tether lines and lazily float up to a height of about 30 feet above his back yard and maybe out across the nearby desert area towards the Mountains, enjoying a few hours of flight before coming back down. But things didn't work out quite as Larry planned... When his friends cut the nylon cords anchoring the chair to the car he did not float lazily up to 30 feet. Instead, he streaked into the Los Angeles sky as if shot from a cannon, pulled aloft by the powerful lift of the helium balloons. He didn't level off at 100 feet, nor did he level off at 1000 feet. After climbing and climbing he levelled off at 16,000 feet. At that height he felt he couldn't risk shooting any of the balloons lest he unbalance the load and really find himself in trouble. So he stayed there, drifting, very cold and frightened, for more than $2^1/_2$ hours.

Then his path crossed the primary approach corridor of Los Angeles International Airport. A TWA pilot first spotted Larry. He radioed the control tower and described passing a guy in a garden chair... with a gun... at 16,000 feet! After a period of some disbelief radar confirmed the existence of an unidentified object floating high above the airport. Eventually Larry gathered the nerve to shoot a few balloons before accidentally dropping the gun, but fortunately by then he had done enough and slowly descended. As he approached the ground the hanging tethers tangled and caught in a power line, resulting in the local electricity authority having to cut off the supply from a Long Beach neighbourhood while Larry was rescued. He eventually managed to climb down to safety where waiting members of the Los Angeles Police Department arrested him. As he was led away a reporter dispatched to cover the daring flight asked him why he had done it. Larry replied nonchalantly, "A man can't just sit around."

Needless to say, Larry doesn't appear to have spent much time studying maths or science at school. Helium is lighter than air and will generate a lift of just under one ounce per cubic foot at sea level (or about 1 gram per litre if you prefer metric measurements). This doesn't sound much, but total lift depends on the number of balloons and their size. The balloons were quite large - around 3.5-4 foot in radius (or 7-8 foot across, based on what Larry said at the time and from

Report developed from contemporary newspaper reports and material published on the Darwin Awards website (www.darwinawards.com) and Mark Barry's more complete "Lawn Chair Pilot" website (http://www.markbarry.com)

Corrections to published material kindly provided by Mark Barry (personal communication). Mark has interviewed several of those present, excluding Larry Walters himself as sadly Larry later took his own life. Photos and an audio track covering the flight are included on the Lawn Chair Pilot web site. The photo here shows Larry shortly after takeoff, having just lost his glasses!

A small number of enthusiasts continue to fly 'cluster balloons' like Larry. See http://www.clusterballoon.org/ for more details

experiments with weights that he and his friends are reported to have conducted). Assuming a 4 foot radius each balloon would hold around 270 cubic feet of helium* and thus generate a lift of over 14lbs (6.4kgs). So 40 or more of these would lift a man, chair and ballast without any problems! But lift is reduced by around 7.5% per 1000 feet, depending on the variations of both pressure and temperature with altitude. So, luckily for Larry, sooner or later he would stop rising...

* see Appendix 1 for details of this calculation

STRUCTURE OF THE BOOK

This is a book for people who want (or need) to analyse practical real-world problems, but are unsure how to proceed with confidence. In an effort to dispel such fears and difficulties I examine and solve a wide variety of real-world problems through a consideration of the processes of measurement and the application of very simple computational methods. This approach enables us to examine, illustrate, test and develop a broad range of ideas and procedures that work, from the comfort of our own 'garden chair', without recourse to complicated equations or programming.

Throughout this book I make use of modern desktop computer systems and the mathematical software that has been developed for them, treating these as a special kind of experimental laboratory. The computer as laboratory enables a quantum leap in our capabilities as number crunchers, professional problem solvers or simply interested amateurs. This is in part a result of the speed of computers, but increasingly as a result of their incorporation of past knowledge and experience - the accumulated results, findings and experience of generations of mathematicians. This experience is stored for our quick reference, embodied in procedures that ensure mistakes are minimised and that 'correct' processes are followed, and then presented to us through interfaces (input and output) that are understandable and visually stimulating. Such facilities do not remove or even reduce the need for understanding and insight – to an extent they demand an even greater level of understanding and care – but they do enable the process of investigation to be far speedier and often to be more effective, rewarding and fun.

In order to explore these issues I have divided this book into three main parts:

Part I deals with the why? why do we mainly use a number system based on 10 elements? why do we have numbers like zero (0) and minus 1 (-1)? why don't we (generally) have a symbol for 10, unlike the Greeks and Romans? why do we have different groups of numbers with strange names like Integers, Imaginaries and Irrationals? and why does mathematics seem to be full of strange symbols and equations? Answering these questions involves delving into some of the history and personalities involved in the development of this subject. It also leads us to look at the history of measurement (of lengths, weights, volumes, times, etc.) and the notions of dimension and connectivity. These are fascinating stories in their own right, but also highlight the role of experimental data in formulating our understanding of numbers and the central role they play in practical and theoretical analysis.

Part II examines the process of discovery through experimentation, focusing on the relatively new world of the computer as laboratory. Computers, and their predecessors electronic and mechanical calculators, and before these vast teams of human 'computers', have long been used to carry out tedious and repetitive numerical processing tasks. But it is a very recent phenomenon that has seen their function developing towards an experimental, interactive, enquiry-led mode of usage. This extends their application beyond that of computational and educational tool, to one in which the tool becomes a key part of the process of discovery and refinement. But our new, computationally rich world, introduces important technical issues that are unfamiliar to most people (except for professional software engineers and some mathematicians). I attempt to address many of these issues, illustrating the materials with a wide range of examples and available software tools. The software tools utilised and discussed include: Microsoft's Excel spreadsheet product; Maplesoft's Maple package, which is particularly good at symbolic processing (working with symbols and expressions as well as numbers); and Waterloo Software's MATLab package (MATrix Laboratory), which is a general purpose scientific suite of software with strong support for manipulation of blocks of numbers and expressions. Student versions of Maple and MATLab are available at much reduced prices. Finally, use is made of several innovative online (web-accessible) tools, which are described and discussed in the text. For all of us wishing to use computers the first step is to be able to enter numbers and expressions, obtain meaningful output, and to incorporate these results into documents. The latter requirement presents a number of difficulties, so I also have included a discussion of some of these issues at the end of Part II.

Part III of this book provides a more detailed look at a selection of numbers and number sequences that are widely regarded as 'interesting'. Some argue that all numbers are interesting, and if a number appears uninteresting it is simply our failure to discover its possibilities. In fact there is a simple, but rather weak 'proof' that there are no uninteresting numbers. However, it is not practical to examine every possible number, nor even a large selection, so I focus on a personally selected subset. Many interesting numbers have even more interesting stories associated with them, and some of these are provided in the final Part of the book.

A selection of suggested books to read, web sites to explore and software to use are provided in Appendix 2 at the end of this book. In addition, on the author's web site (www.mdesmith.com) you will find copies of spreadsheets, program extracts, useful web links, additional materials and sample problems.

INTENDED AUDIENCE

I have written this book to be of help and interest to a wide range of readers: for those interested in learning a little more about numbers, mathematics and computer tools in general; for those who are simply seeking a refresher course with a modern perspective; for those who find mathematics and computing a rather daunting but necessary part of the modern world that they wish to understand more thoroughly; and for those interested in using computers as tools of discovery - examining, testing and visualising information and ideas in new ways. To this extent the text may serve as introductory reading for students (and hence as a resource for teachers and lecturers) including those in higher and further education (colleges, universities). It is intended to be of particular value to those studying subjects in the social sciences, physical and earth sciences, and life sciences. Such disciplines demand a thorough appreciation of mathematical and statistical ideas but incorporate very little pure mathematics or software engineering in their coursework.

Although I discuss and make use of some simple mathematics, this is not a maths text and does not assume a detailed knowledge of this subject. Readers who are more confident in some of these areas may find that they can skim through several of the Sections, in particular those dealing with the different groups of numbers that we commonly encounter. Frequent use is made of software tools, but once again little or no knowledge of programming is required. I do, however, explain the principal forms of notation and conventions used in mathematics, and some of those that apply within computing. It is useful to understand where this notation comes from and how it is used in order to be able to read and appreciate these subjects more fully. Thus, in the process of exploring numbers and data, I cover a wide range of topics including many important mathematical concepts – from number theory to topology, and from basic statistics to calculus, but introduced in an accessible and largely non-traditional manner.

This book also explores a wide range of application areas, from understanding gravity to computing the speed of light, from Internet security to digital audio and image processing, and from the exploration of number series to better ways of obtaining arithmetic results. My hope is that readers will find the material both interesting and enjoyable, and will become confident enough as a result to read more widely in this field, to conduct their own experiments with numbers and to explore the wonderful array of resources now available on the Internet. Amongst the latter is the MacTutor web site of University of St Andrews. This site provides bibliographic details of many famous mathematicians and brief discussions on key topics in mathematics. With their kind permission I have used some of their excellent material in the provision of brief profiles of several key figures from the history of this subject.

When reading this book it is useful to have a pencil and paper to hand, and if possible, have access to a desktop computer to reproduce and test out many of the examples. I make frequent use of Microsoft Excel as a form of sophisticated calculator, so limited familiarity with Excel is helpful but not a pre-requisite. An essential component of this book is the use of many worked examples, including those involving measurement of the physical world. If in doubt (or even if not) I strongly recommend that readers try reproducing the numerical examples, looking for any errors, weaknesses or unstated assumptions.

PART I: FOUNDATIONS

Browsing along the shelves of a library I once came across a set of four books entitled "The World of Mathematics" by James R Newman. Each book had a summation symbol printed on its spine, identifying the volume number, 1, 2, 3 and 4:

I took down the first volume, opened it at random (page 370) and read the following text of a letter, dated January 16th 1913, to a Cambridge mathematician G H Hardy (1877-1947):

> "Dear Sir,
> I beg to introduce myself as a clerk in the Accounts Department of the Port Trust Office at Madras on a salary of only £20 per annum. I am now about 23 years of age [in fact he was 25]. I have no University education but I have undergone the ordinary school course. After leaving school I have been employing the spare time at my disposal to work at Mathematics. I have not trodden through the conventional course which is followed in a University course, but I am striking out a new path for myself....
>
> I would request that you go through the enclosed papers. Being poor, if you are convinced that there is anything of value I would like to have my theorems published... Being inexperienced I would very highly value any advice you give me. Requesting to be excused for the trouble I give you,
> I remain Dear Sir, yours truly,
> S Ramanujan."

Hardy found the 120 or so results enclosed with the letter extraordinary. Many of these he had no idea how to confirm, but they were so original he wrote back to Ramanujan congratulating him on his work and confirming that he would try and help him.

Replying to Hardy's letter Ramanujan wrote:

> "I have found a friend in you who views my labours sympathetically. I am already a half starving man. To preserve my brains I want food and this is my first consideration. Any

sympathetic letter from you will be helpful to me here to get a scholarship either from the university or from the government."

In May that year Hardy arranged for him to come to Cambridge on a substantial Scholarship, including a generous allowance for his family remaining in India. Ramanujan came to England and worked alongside Hardy and his colleagues at Cambridge University on a wide range of mathematical problems before continuing ill-health seriously weakened him. Early in 1918 he was elected as a Fellow of the Royal Society and a Fellow of Trinity College Cambridge. In March 1919, ill once more, he returned to India and died there, aged 33 in 1920.

I found this extraordinary and poignant story captivating, and it encouraged me to read many more of the unusual tales that lie behind much of our modern-day science, philosophy and mathematics — we might speculate that if a largely uneducated, sick, poverty-stricken clerk from a backwater of India can achieve so much then surely we can all set our sights high, no matter what the apparent obstacles. But to make progress in almost any subject, especially those with a scientific basis, it is first helpful to understand something of the history, foundation stones and terminology used. Once these have been familiarised taking the next steps, to experimentation and analysis, is a far less daunting prospect. This first stage is the aim of the Sections that now follow.

1. UNDERSTANDABLE FEARS!

"There are three kinds of people in the world; those who can count and those who can't." Anon

1.1   Numbers and mathematics

Many people claim to be 'number blind' or cannot 'do maths'. Actually, relatively few people (currently believed to be under 5%) exhibit genuine signs of number blindness – finding little or no meaning in numbers or simple combinations of numbers. This is a condition now known as dyscalculia, broadly similar and sometimes associated with the more commonly understood condition of dyslexia (word blindness). Fear of getting the answer wrong or of being subject to ridicule by classmates or colleagues is a much more common and pervasive phenomenon. And unlike many subjects, there is often a definite right or wrong answer so it is very obvious if we are wrong—we cannot bluff our way past this apparently universal truth.

If you were to ask 100 people which subject they liked least at school, or which they found the most frightening or difficult, the great majority would say Maths (or Math if you ask an American audience). Despite the fact that learning a foreign language or musical instrument may well be at least as difficult, if not more so, there is some kind of deeply held fear of mathematics amongst the population at large. This is not based on a fear of numbers, but of the way in which problems that involve numbers seem to need to be turned into symbols and equations (a process known as abstraction) in order to obtain the 'right' answer – or wrong answer for most of us, which is the real cause of our concern! It is clearly far too easy to get things wrong so many avoid the subject altogether.

But if you ask the same 100 people a different question, perhaps one of a more practical nature, such as "how much sales tax (or VAT in Europe) is payable on an item costing 100 pounds (or dollars or euros)?" most would be able to answer immediately, assuming they knew the relevant tax rate. So, for example, given a dress or suit costing £100.00 in the UK, before VAT has been added, nearly everyone will be able to tell you that the dress or suit will actually cost you £117.50, since this figure now includes the £17.50 of VAT which must be added to the basic price (the UK rate being 17.5%). We know this answer is correct because the sums involved are very easy – we can work it out by a simple *forwards* calculation, using multiplication, i.e. £100 x 17.5% = £17.50 plus the original £100 gives the answer.

It turns out that the opposite or inverse process, division, is much more difficult. I could have asked the question above the other way around: for example, "given a dress or suit costing £100 including sales tax/VAT, how much is the cost of the dress or suit *excluding* VAT". Well, the answer is clearly not £82.50, because that would mean the VAT was £17.50 which was the answer when the dress or suit cost £117.50 including VAT — in fact the answer to this new question must be more than £82.50, and is actually £85.11 (to the nearest whole penny), with VAT amounting to £14.89.

To obtain this solution we either need to work things out backwards, i.e. starting with the total and working back to the component parts using division (the inverse of multiplication), or we need to carry out a series of guesses, working forwards from pairs of guesses (e.g. £80, £90) that we are confident lie either side of the true answer. We then systematically reduce the interval until we are as close as possible to the correct value (see Box 1 for a detailed look at this process and Box 2 for some historical context).

In the example we have been using the quick solution simply involves dividing the price including VAT, i.e. the £100, by 1.175 and rounding the answer to the nearest penny — not that easy by hand. The number 1.175 is used because this is 100% plus 17.5%, i.e. 117.5/100. To make use of this result we need to be comfortable with fractions and division, whereas the forwards approach and the guessing methods only require multiplication and need minimal understanding of fractions. Perhaps the world is divided into people (and computers as it happens) who can do fractions and those who can't! In practice fractions and percentages are not too difficult and they are so widely used in everyday life that this is one area that is really worth getting to understand: whether it is the price of a dress; deciding how much to tip in a restaurant; seeing how much interest a bank is charging you; or looking at the success rate of a new medical procedure. All share a common basic form — a systematic, tried and tested procedure for obtaining the correct answer using a well-defined series of steps. Such procedures are known as *algorithms* (see also, Box 2).

Our understandable fear of numbers and mathematics can be diminished (or maybe even cured) if we are aware of some important facts that we are not normally told. The first is that we can understand and solve many problems by experimentation, in particular by numerical experimentation — getting one's hands dirty, actually playing with numbers, patterns, diagrams and now, using computers, in order to see what happens and get a feel for the how? and the why? The second key fact is to appreciate that it has taken thousands of years of work and the brightest minds in history to get to where we are today, and there have been long periods (hundreds of years) when little or no progress was made at all. So we shouldn't be too despondent if we find even quite 'simple' problems difficult — we need to be patient — listening, experimenting, and learning, and then applying and testing our procedures. If the testing shows our answer is wrong, we need to go back and identify why, and then try to resolve the problem. Doing mathematics is a bit like sitting on a wall: everything on one side — the things you have already learnt or discovered — seem trivial; whilst everything on the other side, as yet undiscovered, seem unimaginably difficult!

The last point to make is that most professional and academic scientists and mathematicians find many areas of mathematics really hard to understand, if not impossible. This is for several

---

Box 1. Simple search algorithm for finding the sales tax on a £100 item

---

Let's start by using our initial guesses for the dress or suit price of £80 and £90 before sales tax is added: with £80 we get a total price for the dress or suit of £94 including sales tax at 17.5% (£80 + £80x17.5% which is £14) so this is too low. With £90 we get £105.75 - too high. So next we might try 'chopping' our initial range in half to £85 next, which would be very close to the correct answer. We would find £85 is a little too low, so we could halve the new upper interval (£85-£90) and look at £87.50, continuing this process until we have homed in the right answer (stopping when the result equals £100.00, rounded to the nearest 1p). The complete sequence in this example is shown in the following table created in Excel:

Guesses, excl VAT, £	VAT @ 17.5% (to 2 decimal places, dp)	Price, incl VAT, £
80.00	14.00	94.00
90.00	15.75	105.75
85.00	14.88	99.875
87.50	15.31	102.8125
86.25	15.09	101.3438
85.625	14.98	100.6094
85.3125	14.93	100.2422
85.15625	14.90	100.0586
85.07813	14.89	99.9668
85.11719	14.90	100.0127
85.09766	14.89	99.98975
85.10742	14.89	100.0012

In this case the procedure is known as a binary chop algorithm. The reader might be surprised to know that many computers perform accurate division using an algorithm that involves a combination of guessing the answer and then seeking better and better approximations, rather than applying the kinds of rules for long division we learnt at school. I describe such procedures in more detail in Part II.

---

reasons. The first is that the term 'mathematics' is more like the term 'languages' than say any specific language such as 'French' or 'Latin'. Mathematics involves use of a (very large) set of distinct and often little known languages, accepting however that most have common foundations. Just as no-one can speak or read every language in the world, so no one person can read or understand all fields of mathematics — the languages (notations, rules of grammar, etc.) are frequently so different that even the best mathematicians can master only a few. Some people are definitely better at mathematics than others, and some are even brilliant at it, but this is not so different from skill as a musician or composer, or in creating fantastic sculpture, or conversing fluently in many foreign tongues.

In addition to this multi-lingual view of the subject there is a big problem of what we mean by the word truth. Earlier I said that it was only natural to fear ridicule if you get the answer wrong, because in this field you are either right or wrong. But this is not actually the case — or at least, not always. It turns out that for some problems we simply cannot determine whether a particular

---

Box 2. Mohammed ibn Musa al-Khowârizmî (c.780-850AD)

"Mohammed, son of Moses, from Khowârizmî". Khowârizmî is now known as the province and town of Khiva in Uzbekistan, north of modern day Iraq

---

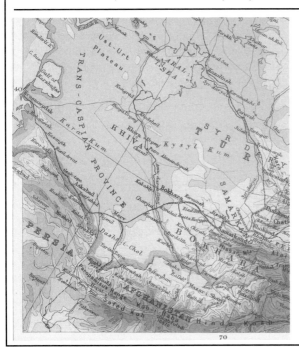

The Arab astronomer al-Khowârizmî (spelt in various ways in the Latin alphabet) wrote a book in c. 830 AD entitled 'Hisâb Al-jabr w'al muqabâla' which roughly translates as 'the science of restoring [the balance in an equation] and simplification'. Our word Algebra comes from Europeanisation of the word Al-jabr in the title of this book when it was trans-lated into Latin in the 12th century. The word Al-jabr also meant bone-setting, and even in the early 20th century barbers signs in Spain advertised 'Algebrista y Sangrador', or 'bone-setting and blood-letting'. Our word Algorithm comes from the author's name (actually where he came from) transliterated into Latin as al-Goritmi or algoritmi and thence algorithm. Initially this meant to 'compute with positional notation', but this developed over time into its modern day usage.

---

answer or proposition is true or false; in other instances we may know that a 'true' or 'best' answer exists but is unachievable; and in very many cases there is either no known answer, multiple possible answers (possibly infinitely many), answers that make no apparent sense, or no clear agreement on what the answer should be. We should take comfort from these observations, because it shows that common sense and experience, based on results and usefulness rather than some idea of absolute truth, is often (but not always) a good way forwards.

So now we know that one of the keys to working with numbers is experimentation and testing, and that often there is not just a single, 'true' answer to a question, even if it appears to be relatively straightforward. We also know that for centuries, notably since the time of Descartes and Newton in the 17th century, people have been experimenting, learning from the results, and writing down rules and procedures that work — providing the building blocks from which we can continue construction without recourse to re-doing all of their work. Once this methodology was discovered and written down (and printed) in a form that was clear to a wide range of readers, progress was very rapid. This applies for almost every subject, especially those that have a scientific bias.

It is also true that occasionally some of the intermediate building blocks or even foundation stones turn out to be faulty. As a result, these may have to be discarded and everything constructed upon them questioned and possibly rejected. Alternatively we may be able to take a pragmatic view and accept that despite their failings, the results are so useful that we can ignore their weaknesses for most if not all problems. So called 'pure mathematicians' often dislike this situation, seeking clarity and certainty in every aspect of their subject, whereas 'applied mathematicians' tend to be more accepting of the weaknesses, as long as the job in hand gets done and always works in practice. By 'always works' is meant that the answers are good enough for the problem at hand, or 'fit for purpose', and have never or very rarely been found to go wrong in practice. Newton's laws of motion are a good example, which remain incredibly useful despite fundamental changes to the underlying logic being introduced by Einstein two centuries later. Rather like baking a cake, it also usually means that starting with the same set of values (ingredients) and the same procedures (preparation and cooking method), the same or very nearly the same answer (cake) will be produced — even if someone else does the cooking! Finally, as if to knock the pure mathematicians off their pedestal, it was shown in the 1930s that there are some 'cakes' that should be possible to bake given a set of ingredients and procedures, but turn out to be impossible to cook.

1.2   Statistics

"If there is a 50-50 chance that something can go wrong, then 9 times out of 10 it will", Anon

So we have started to address the fear of numbers and mathematics, but what about statistics? People often admire mathematicians but almost all dislike or distrust statistics and thereby, statisticians. Actually there are two quite separate aspects to this understandable response: the first relates to the use of selected numbers or "statistics", often by politicians or the media that claim to "explain" some fact or justify a particular point of view. We are right to be deeply suspicious about almost all such information, however presented, as we shall see in some examples below. The second relates to the branch of mathematics that collects, analyses, manipulates and reports on data — i.e. information that has been collected in some way from the world around us. In this context 'statistics' is simply another language in the broad collection that is mathematics. And like many such languages it has its own rules, notation and history. What makes it different, and perhaps explains the dislike of it amongst many students who leave school and go through higher education on the road to a career in a scientific, medical or technical (SMT) discipline, is that they are obliged to study statistics as part of their degree courses.

So why does statistics cause so much concern and distrust? Essentially, just as specific numbers and groups of numbers are the stuff of mathematics, so a selection of numbers from a larger set is the basis of statistics (sampling). The process of selection, the definition of what comprises the larger set and the subsequent description of these sets are the factors that cause most of the

Table 1-1 Regional employment data — grouping affects

	Employed (000s)	Unemployed (000s)	Total (000s) (Unemployed %)
Area A			
European	81	9	90 (10%)
Asian	9	1	10 (10%)
Total	90	10	100 (10%)
Area B			
European	40	10	50 (20%)
Asian	40	10	50 (20%)
Total	80	20	100 (20%)
Areas A and B			
European	121	19	140 (13.6%)
Asian	49	11	60 (18.3%)
Total	170	30	200 (15%)

problems. And once a selection has been made, there is endless scope for confusion and misinformation! For example, look at the employment statistics shown in Table 1-1.

Areas A and B both contain a total of 100,000 people who are classified as either employed or not. In area A 10% of both Europeans and Asians are unemployed (i.e. equal proportions), and likewise in Area B we have equal proportions (this time 20% unemployed). So we expect that combining areas A and B will give us 200,000 people, with an equal proportion of Europeans and Asians unemployed (we would guess this to be 15%), but it is not the case — 13.6% of Europeans and 18.3% of Asians are seen to be unemployed! The reason for this unexpected result is that in Area A there are many more Europeans than Asians, so we are working from different total populations. With statistics you have to know exactly how the information has been constructed in order to make any sense of it — so-called "headline statistics" are at best of little value and at worst, totally misleading.

The same logic applies to graphs — line diagrams that show values (such as average income per person) changing against time for example. To be meaningful a statistical graph should tell you:

(i)   what the scales are

(ii) whether it starts at zero or some other value, and

(iii) how it was calculated, in particular exactly what data set and time period it is based upon.

Without all of these elements the information presented should be viewed with caution.

The final problem I wish to refer to relating to statistical data is a very general one, but again an issue that is little understood. This is the problem that once sets of numbers have been added together and totals or averages given, you can no longer safely use this information to make specific inferences about the original numbers (and vice versa). For example, suppose we have two adjacent areas, A and B, each containing 100 people in employment. Suppose now that 100 people in area A each earn 1000 Euros/week and those in area B each earn 500 Euros/week. Then combining the information we have 200 people in a slightly larger area, and we might be tempted to say that people on average earn 750 Euros/week. But as we know, nobody in areas A or B earns 750 Euros/week. It is acceptable to say that the average earnings in the combined area are 750 Euros/week, but it is not correct to say that individuals in this area earn this amount. This is quite a subtle point and is known as the *ecological fallacy*. Recent examples of this kind of fallacy include: the observation that breast cancer rates are higher in countries that have a high fat content in their diet, and then suggesting that women who eat more fat in their diet are more likely to suffer from breast cancer; or that crime rates are higher in areas of high unemployment, and then stating that it is the unemployed who are responsible for most crimes. The inferences drawn may be valid, and such observations can provide very useful pointers for research, but the data only provides very tenuous support for the claims made.

There is a more obvious twin (or dual) of this problem, known as the *atomist fallacy*. In this case we might find that some people (individuals, 'atoms') earn 500 Euros/week and then suggest that this is true generally, i.e. that (almost) everyone earns this amount, which we also know is incorrect. Most of us are familiar with such claims from the popular press and occasionally from more reputable sources.

Issues such as these are amongst the main reasons that the techniques and models used in statistics are found by many students to be particularly difficult. Because of the many pitfalls, statistical techniques have been devised to summarise information, identify patterns and describe relationships based upon well-defined rules and assumptions. As a result these rules and models can be quite complex and if the assumptions are not met, the techniques and results are either not valid or have limited use.

So, as you knew all along, statistics is a tricky subject, full of pitfalls and requiring great care. Hopefully the comments I have made in this Section go some way to explaining why some of these problems occur, helping you to know what to look for in future.

2   CORE COMPONENTS

"'I only took the regular course'. 'What was that?' inquired Alice. 'Reeling and Writhing, of course, to begin with', the Mock Turtle replied; 'and then the different branches of Arithmetic — Ambition, Distraction, Uglification, and Derision'." from The Mock Turtle's Story, Alice's Adventures in Wonderland, Lewis Carroll, 1865

This chapter describes many of the common forms of notation and symbolism used in mathematics and computing, and how these came into modern usage. It also addresses issues such as accuracy and precision, explaining these in the context of modern computer systems. Readers who are confident of this material may feel comfortable glancing through this chapter and then proceeding rapidly to Chapter 3, which deals with problems of measurement.

2.1   Notation and punctuation

One of the biggest problems when working with numbers relates to the way numbers, and expressions that relate to numbers (such as equations), are written down. 'Reeling and Writhing' often seems an appropriate description of the complexities and confusions that may arise. Getting it wrong can easily result in 'Derision'!

With the widespread use of computers in the home and at work, coupled with the growing internationalism (globalisation) of communications, it is becoming essential to understand how and why numerical information is represented in particular ways. Obtaining a better understanding of these questions provides us with an appreciation of the similarities and differences in such matters around the world, and reduces our reticence to work with and explore numerical problems. Adopting a consistent, formal system of writing for numbers and operations on numbers has taken a very long time — thousands of years — and even today there are ongoing debates as to how numbers and equations should be written, stored on computers and displayed on screen and paper. In fact the answer in many cases is to accept the differences and to facilitate multiple forms of information presentation for input and output purposes, whilst ensuring a consistent and 'complete' internal representation of the information is retained within the computer.

Most countries now use a decimal or base10 number system, with its origin in our 10 fingered hands (we have 10 digits). This does not prevent us from working with other bases, such as 2 (binary, using the symbols 1 and 0), 5 (one hand at a time), 16 (hexadecimal, using the symbols 0...9 plus A B C D E F) or 60 (sexigesimal or Babylonian, useful in time and angle measurement). But these are not usually the written form used for numbers. Even within the decimal system the representation of numbers may not necessarily use the familiar (Arabic) digits 1,2...,9,0. For example, most Arab countries use a slightly different system of notation, known as Indic, in place of or in addition to the so-called Arabic numerals:

١٢٣٤٥٦٧٨٩٠

It is interesting to see that in this system the digit 5 is represented by a symbol that looks like 0, and the symbol for 0 is simply a raised form of dot. And there remains scope for confusion when familiar number symbols are hand-written, as is common between 2 and Z, 1 and 7 and I, 0 and O. If letters and numbers are assigned unique codes, however, such confusion should be avoidable. Perhaps the first attempt to define a set of 'digital' codes to represent numbers and letters was made by the mathematician C F Gauss and his colleague W Weber, from the Physics Department at Göttingen University in Germany, in 1833. Their code table is shown in Figure 2.1, where R means Right and L means Left, indicating the direction a magnetic needle turned when an electric current was enabled on a long wire between two buildings. This coding system provides 32 values (2x2x2x2x2 or 2^5, i.e. 5 bits). Some symbols having dual meanings (G/J) and X is omitted. With 26 letters and 10 digits and a Space character this would have required 37 values, which would have involved an extra bit in the code, so some simplifications were made. Note that this pre-dates Morse Code or the first telex machines.

In 1870 J M E Baudot patented a new coding scheme that sought to overcome the limited set of characters and functions available with 5-bit schemes. He introduced the idea of using 2 of the 32

RRRRR	A	RLLLL	1
RRRRL	B	RRLLR	2
RRRLR	C	RLRLL	3
RRLRR	D	RLLRL	4
RLRLR	E	LLLRR	5
LRRRR	F	RLLRR	6
LRLRR	G/J	LLLRL	7
RLRRL	H	LLRRL	8
LLRLL	I/Y	LRRLR	9
LRRRL	K	LRLLR	0
RLRRR	L		
RRLLL	M		
LLLLL	N		
LRLLL	O		
LRLRL	P		
LLRRR	Q		
RRRLL	R		
RRLRL	S/Z		
LLRLR	T		
RLLLR	U		
LRRLL	V		
LLLLR	W		

Figure 2.1 Gauss and Weber telegraph code

available codes to indicate that all subsequent codes were either: (a) Letters only; or (b) Numbers, symbols and functions only. The sequences he chose were equivalent to RRRRR and RRLRR in Gauss-Weber coding or 11111 and 11011 in binary, and are sometimes known as SHIFT sequences (based on comparison with early mechanical typewriters). In this way he extended the Gauss-Weber code to provide up to 62 (=64-2) usable codes. So, for example, if we call 11111 (SI) and 11011 (SO) we could code the text "The number 52 is a secret!" using something like:

(SO)THE NUMBER (SI)52(SO) IS A SECRET (SI)!

Notice that only uppercase (Capitals) OR lowercase was possible, not both. As well as supporting new characters, such as ! and ?, new features were provided by Baudot's code, including Line Feed (LF, coded as 00010) and Carriage Return (CR, coded as 01000). These enabled remote printers to layout the information being transmitted as a series of lines.

This form of coding continued in use for many years, but it too required extension, ideally by a more powerful coding scheme. In order to provide a character set, symbols, case selection and other facilities required by computers and word processors, the coding scheme known as ASCII (American Standard Code for Information Interchange) was developed. It is one of a family of digital coding systems in use today (see ASCII table, Table 2-1). ASCII dates from 1963 when it was first introduced as a 7-bit code, and then from 1968 as the 8-bit version we now use. There are around 180 national variants of ASCII registered with the International Standards Organisation (ISO).

In order to represent complex expressions or unusual mathematical symbols with a limited set of codes, quite sophisticated rules are required to define how combinations of these basic codes are to be interpreted. As we shall see in Part II, special 'languages' and toolsets such as TeX and MathML exist to address this problem, for example using the bracketed sequence of ASCII characters {\sum} to mean use the symbol Σ.

2.2   Number systems

"...don't panic. Base eight is just like base ten really — if you're missing two fingers."
Tom Lehrer's song 'New Math'

Individual numbers are typically written from left to right, even in cultures where the written form goes from right to left or up and down. The number order matters, with the leftmost digit being that with the largest value. In decimal systems, each position is 10 times the size of the position one to its right whilst in binary systems each number is twice the value of its rightmost neighbour. Thus in decimal notation the number 183 means 1*100 plus 8*10 plus 3*1 (where the symbol * means 'times' or 'multiplied by'). This is an example of a positional number system and

Table 2-1 ASCII Codeset — 8-bit

Decimal	Binary	Character	Decimal	Binary	Character
032	00100000	SPACE	080	01010000	P
033	00100001	!	081	01010001	Q
034	00100010		082	01010010	R
035	00100011	#	083	01010011	S
036	00100100	$	084	01010100	T
037	00100101	%	085	01010101	U
038	00100110	&	086	01010110	V
039	00100111	'	087	01010111	W
040	00101000	(	088	01011000	X
041	00101001	)	089	01011001	Y
042	00101010	*	090	01011010	Z
043	00101011	+	091	01011011	[
044	00101100	,	092	01011100	\
045	00101101	-	093	01011101	]
046	00101110	.	094	01011110	^
047	00101111	/	095	01011111	_
048	00110000	0	096	01100000	`
049	00110001	1	097	01100001	a
050	00110010	2	098	01100010	b
051	00110011	3	099	01100011	c
052	00110100	4	100	01100100	d
053	00110101	5	101	01100101	e
054	00110110	6	102	01100110	f
055	00110111	7	103	01100111	g
056	00111000	8	104	01101000	h
057	00111001	9	105	01101001	i
058	00111010	:	106	01101010	j
059	00111011	;	107	01101011	k
060	00111100	<	108	01101100	l
061	00111101	=	109	01101101	m
062	00111110	>	110	01101110	n
063	00111111	?	111	01101111	o
064	01000000	@	112	01110000	p
065	01000001	A	113	01110001	q
066	01000010	B	114	01110010	r
067	01000011	C	115	01110011	s
068	01000100	D	116	01110100	t
069	01000101	E	117	01110101	u
070	01000110	F	118	01110110	v
071	01000111	G	119	01110111	w
072	01001000	H	120	01111000	x
073	01001001	I	121	01111001	y
074	01001010	J	122	01111010	z
075	01001011	K	123	01111011	{
076	01001100	L	124	01111100	|
077	01001101	M	125	01111101	}
078	01001110	N	126	01111110	~
079	01001111	O	127	01111111	DELETE

dates from around 600AD in India and less than a century later in the Arab world, from which it was subsequently communicated to Mediterranean and northern European cultures. For special purposes collections of numbers are sometimes written in blocks, which I discuss in more detail a bit later on (Section 2.4).

The symbols we use for writing or displaying numbers are generally called "glyphs", and vary across the world, much as written languages vary in the alphabets or composite graphics used (such as hieroglyphs or Chinese characters). In Ancient Egypt, although they developed base10 number systems, these were non-positional systems with different hieroglyphs for separate powers of 10 and symbols repeated in blocks rather than on a line for multiples less than 10.

Zero was introduced as a placeholder initially. If a number is written in positional form and there is no placeholder, when a column is missing it causes confusion. For example, the number 305 could be written as 3 5 if we had no placeholder for the 10s, but is this really 305, or maybe 35 or 3005 written without sufficient care? The number system of the Babylonians suffered from this problem. The solution, dating from around the 2nd or 3rd century BC in India and from the 7th century AD in the Arab world, was to add a symbol, at first a dot and then a small circle, ∘ , to identify the empty column. Subsequently it was found useful to have a symbol for zero which could be used in algebraic operations, such as $x+0=x$, $y-z=0$, or q times $0=0$. The Italian mathematician Leonardo of Pisa, also known as Fibonacci (see Box 3), is regarded as being responsible for introducing the use of zero in Europe, in 1202 AD. The words zero and cipher both derive from the Arabic word as-sifr (meaning empty), which Fibonacci transliterated as zephirum. The equals symbol, =, was introduced much later, in 1557, by Welshman Robert Recorde.

In modern Western decimal (Indo-Arabic) notation the number 111 means 1*100 plus 1*10 plus 1*1 (or $1*10^2+1*10^1+1*10^0$), whereas in binary (base2) this number means 1*4 plus 1*2 plus 1*1 (or $1*2^2+1*2^1+1*2^0$) i.e. 7 in decimal notation. The same rules apply for any other base, such as base8 (octal), base16 (hex), or base60. Numbers less than 1 are treated in the same way, but with a separator (generally displayed as a full stop or 'period') to indicate the break in values. For example, 0.111 in base10 arithmetic means

$$1*\frac{1}{10}+1*\frac{1}{100}+1*\frac{1}{1000}$$

whereas in binary it equates to the decimal fraction 7/8, because it means

$$1*\frac{1}{2}+1*\frac{1}{4}+1*\frac{1}{8}$$

Whilst computers generally work in binary, for simplicity and speed, input and output is handled in the form we are most familiar with or explicitly choose, and the computer simply converts this to and fro without us having to worry about the processes involved.

Box 3. Fibonacci, or Leonardo of Pisa (c.1170 or 1175 to 1240 or 1250)

Fibonacci (*filius* i.e. son of Bonacci) was born in Italy but was educated in North Africa where his father was posted. He travelled widely with his father and recognised the enormous advantages of the mathematical systems used in the countries they visited. The head of the statue of Fibonacci shown here was completed in 1863 and is sited near the Leaning Tower in Pisa, Northern Italy. The image is not based on any portraits or statues of Fibonacci, since none are known to exist.

Fibonacci ended his travels around the year 1200 and at that time he returned to Pisa. There he wrote a number of texts that played an important role in reviving ancient mathematical skills and he made significant contributions of his own. Fibonacci lived in the days before printing, so his books were hand written and the only way to have a copy of one of his books was to have another hand-written copy made. Of his books we still have copies of Liber abaci (1202), Practica geometriae (1220), Flos (1225), and Liber quadratorum. Given that relatively few hand-made copies would ever have been produced, we are fortunate to have access to his writing in these works. However, we know that he wrote some other texts that unfortunately are lost. The book "Liber abaci", introduced the Hindu-Arabic place-valued decimal system and the use of Arabic numerals into Europe. Indeed, although mainly a book about the use of Arab numerals (which became known as *algorism*, see Box 2), simultaneous linear equations are also studied in this work. Certainly many of the problems that Fibonacci considers in Liber abaci were similar to those appearing in Arab sources.

A problem in the third section of Liber abaci led to the introduction of the Fibonacci numbers and the Fibonacci sequence for which Fibonacci is best remembered today: "A certain man put a pair of rabbits in a place surrounded on all sides by a wall. How many pairs of rabbits can be produced from that pair in a year if it is supposed that every month each pair begets a new pair which from the second month on becomes productive?" The total number of pairs of rabbits at the end of each month is given by the sequence 1, 1, 2, 3, 5, 8, 13, 21, 34, 55,... (Fibonacci omitted the first term in Liber abaci). This sequence, in which each number is the sum of the two preceding numbers, has proved extremely fruitful and appears in many different areas of mathematics and science (see further, Section 15.3).

But what about 1/3? Written in decimal form this is 0.3333... the three dots indicating that there are an unlimited number of similar digits to the right, and the same is true for binary, where it is 0.010101010..., again a repeating number. In base3, however, 1/3 is simply 0.10000... because the first digit after the point represents precisely one third. So the choice of base affects the way in which numbers are stored, and how many digits are needed to correctly represent the information. However, for two main reasons this observation does not help us. The first reason is that for most practical purposes we have to choose one format or base for storing our data, and this tends to be binary. It is impractical to store information in many different formats and switch between them at will or in some kind of super-intelligent manner. The second reason is that some numbers cannot be represented by a finite number of digits, no matter what base is chosen, i.e. they show an ever changing and everlasting pattern of digits (or lack of pattern) no matter how we describe or store them. Numbers of this type are discussed further in Section 5.3. Readers will realise that a problem with computers is that once a number such as 1/3 is stored as a very long binary sequence it is almost impossible to reverse the process, i.e. recognising that it is really 1/3. It is also clear that there is a limit to the number of digits that computers can store, so they will almost always store some numbers inaccurately.

The widespread convention is that positional number systems operate horizontally, from left to right. This can present problems for languages that are written from right to left. For example, if you are typing on a computer in Hebrew and start to enter a number, the software will normally switch the direction or mode of screen display, typically 'pushing' the numbers from right to left whilst leaving the active position or flashing *cursor* at the right hand end of the number. When you start typing text again the cursor will leap back over the number typed to the left hand end of the text. The left to right convention is not used in a consistent manner for numeric dates, such as 12/09/2004 (meaning the 12th of September 2004 in Europe, but the 9th of December 2004 in North America) whereas it is applied for times, 3:30 PM or 15:30 hrs. It would make more sense if dates were always written in YYYY/MM/DD order, e.g. 2004/09/12, and this would certainly help numeric sorting of such date strings, but this arrangement is less common (see further, Section 4 which deals with Times and Dates).

Similar issues arise with negative numbers and expressions. Negative numbers are usually displayed with either a preceding minus sign (-) or may be shown in brackets or a different colour (e.g. red) for financial applications. In some cultures the order of operations, including those involving subtractions, retains the language order. Thus in Arabic, A-B typically means subtract A from B rather than B from A, although this would normally only apply when the relation is written or typed using Arabic characters. Likewise the expression w=s-n would appear in Arabic in the reverse order (i.e. right to left) as:

و = س - ن

Within computers the need to store a minus symbol for most numbers (so-called *signed* numbers as opposed to *un-signed* numbers) often results in an extra position being required in memory or on disk, the "sign bit". This requirement reduces the maximum size of number that a computer can store directly — since each bit (BInary digiT) provides a multiple of 2, the effect of having signed numbers is to halve the size of the maximum stored number. Such issues are discussed in more detail in Section 2.8, which covers Precision and Accuracy.

Modern number systems are positional and as we have seen, both the order and position of the numbers has significance. This was not always the case. Before the Arabic-based positional system was widely adopted the notations used by Roman, Greek and the majority of earlier civilisations were based on ordered but non-positional systems. Complex numerical operations using this arrangement would be extremely time consuming and prone to error. In practice, these cultures did not use their written number systems for most of their direct calculations or mathematical analyses. Instead they used words and drawings (geometric diagrams for example) for problem solving, and several versions of the abacus for arithmetic operations — for example using counting pebbles, or *calculi*, from whence we get the terms *calculate* and *calculus* (and, incidentally, calcium and calcify). Interestingly, if you are ever unfortunate enough to suffer from kidney stones or gall stones, which are both very painful conditions, the doctors still refer to these as *calculi* because they are often calciferous.

However, getting back to early number systems, addition is actually quite simple using Roman numerals and similar systems. For example the addition sum 585+59 in Roman numerals is DLXXXV + LIX and all we need to do is add up similar letters and write the result down, so we have DLLXXXXIV or the equivalent DCXLIV because L+L=C (where D=500, C=100, L=50, X=10, V=5, and I=1) and XL can be used in place of XXXX. The largest number that was written in Roman numerals using a single letter was M=1000, but still larger numbers were needed. A variety of special graphical symbols were adopted for 10,000 and 100,000, and in some cases lines drawn above a number would indicate multiplication by 1,000. Examples of these conventions are illustrated in Figure 2.2.

Roman characters (the main Western alphabet) are used in expressions and equations in many ways, but the widespread convention is that characters from the end of the alphabet, such as *x, y* and *z* are used for variables — objects that may represent a variety of specific values or numbers — whilst characters from the start of the alphabet, *a, b, c* etc. are used for known or unknown constants, such as 3 or 2.4. This convention is due to the French mathematician and philosopher, René Descartes (see further, Box 4) who wrote down these guidelines and many others that we continue to use today, in the early 17th century.

Greek characters are also widely used in equations, however principally in the West. Their function is to provide an additional set of symbols that are distinct from the Roman alphabet. Typically lower case Greek characters used for variables and for selected *constants* (objects whose values are fixed and pre-defined). Upper case Greek characters are used widely for *operators* (objects that describe how a collection of variables are to be handled).

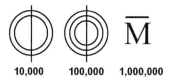

10,000   100,000   1,000,000

Figure 2.2 Representation of large numbers in the Roman system

Examples of the use of Greek lower case characters are:

α (alpha), β (beta), δ and ε (delta and epsilon, often used to indicate very small amounts, i.e. numbers that are very close to 0), γ (gamma, frequently used as a specific Constant), μ (mu, the symbol associated with the population average or mean in statistical parlance), π (pi, perhaps the most famous Constant), and θ and φ (theta and phi, the symbols often used to indicate angular variables).

Eastern societies, such as Japan, China and Korea typically use local symbols or character sets in such cases, rather than Greek, depending often on whether their audience is domestic or international.

Examples of operators that use Greek upper case characters are:

Δ (Delta, widely used to indicate a Difference operation, i.e. to calculate the difference between two values); Γ (Gamma, generally used as an abbreviation for a special function whose values are related to numbers like 5*4*3*2*1, also denoted 5! or 5 *factorial* − Γ is used when calculating *n!* where *n* is a fraction); Π (capital Pi, used to indicate the Product operation, i.e. where a series of numbers or expressions should be *multiplied* together); and Σ (Sigma, the summation operator we came across earlier, used when a series of numbers or expressions should be *added* together).

Box 4. René Descartes (1596-1650)

Descartes was educated at the Jesuit college of La Flèche in Anjou. He entered the college at the age of eight years, just a few months after the opening of the college in January 1604. In 1618 he started studying mathematics and mechanics and began to seek a unified science of nature. After two years in Holland he travelled through Europe. He spent time in 1623 in Paris where he made contact with Mersenne (see Box 7), who kept him in touch with the scientific world for many years. By 1628 he settled in Holland and began work on his first major treatise on physics. This work was near completion when news reached him that Galileo had been condemned to house arrest. Descartes decided not to risk publication at that time, but he was pressed by his friends to publish some of his ideas and he duly wrote a treatise on science which was published in 1637 – an Appendix, *La Géométrie* ("Geometry") is by far the most important part of this work

2.2.1 Cardinal and Ordinal numbers

"Chapters in books are usually given the Cardinal numbers 1,2,3,4,5,6 and so on. But I have decided to give my chapters prime numbers 2,3,5,7,11,13 and so on because I like prime numbers." Christopher Boone, an Asperger's Syndrome boy, aged 15, in Chapter 19 (i.e. 8) in "The curious incident of the dog in the night-time", by Mark Haddon, 2003. Asperger's Syndrome is a form of autism.

The name Cardinal number is usually reserved for numbers that are used for counting. Whilst Arabic numerals are the most widely used in the Western world for dealing with *quantities* — counting and the display of numerical procedures — other forms are used for ordered sequences or series of numbers. Frequently Roman numerals I, II, III, IV, V..., X, etc. or the lower case versions i, ii, iii, iv... are used to indicate an ordered sequence and in this context are called Ordinal Numbers. Western clocks frequently use Roman numerals for displaying the time, but interestingly they normally show IV as IIII — this is believed to be for design reasons (visually balancing the VIII) rather than having any technical or historical basis. Other letters were used by the Romans for larger numbers, such as 50, 100 or 1000 as noted earlier, but there is no Roman symbol for zero or for values less than zero. Likewise, the Hebrew tradition uses letters from their alphabet as numbers in an Ordinal context — for example, for chapter numbers and page numbers in books and for writing the Hebrew calendar. With purely Ordinal numbers the notions of "greater than", >, and less than, <, and equality, =, may make sense (e.g. Chapter V is greater than/after Chapter IV), but numerical operations like addition or division in general are not meaningful.

2.3 Symbols

Symbols such as +, -, x, ÷, = are fairly universal and have consistent meaning, but there is an enormous range of other symbols and combinations of symbols that are used with varying degrees of consistency. To be certain of their meaning one often has to check the context in which they are being used. Even these symbols have had a varied history. For example the symbol now used for division, ÷, was formerly used for subtraction, and even today division is written in many different forms — the last of the forms shown below, with the line separating the top (*numerator*) and bottom (*denominator*), was introduced by Fibonacci:

$$a÷b, \ a/b, \ a:b, \ \frac{a}{b}$$

The symbol /, known as a *solidus*, is used in a variety of contexts: in text it often means 'or' as in "sales tax/VAT" used earlier; or 'per' as in "metres/sec" and, as we shall see later (Section 3.5) in the definition of gravitational acceleration (metres/sec^2). These last two examples are both forms of division, in each case being in terms of units of measure rather than specific numbers. And of course, to complicate matters, / is used as a field separator in web addresses and computer file directory specifications.

The multiplication symbol is sometimes written as a raised dot, $a \cdot b$ or an asterisk, $a*b$ (often in computing). The equals sign, =, which derives from using two lines of the same length, is the source of considerable problems, since $a=b$ can mean that this is an equation, which we may wish to retain or manipulate, or that a should be replaced by b (i.e. an assignment, a is b). This distinction is important in determining what happens next, whether we are working on paper or using a computer. Different symbols are sometimes used for equality and assignment in order to avoid this confusion. Note that whilst for many purposes the order or precedence of operations is left-to-right, assignment is often (but not always) a right-to-left operator.

Examples of other symbolic notation used widely and with broadly consistent meaning include those shown in Figure 2.3. There are a range of national and international standards providing guidance on symbol usage, including the International Standards Organisation (ISO) standard ISO6862:1996 and the USA ANSI standard ANSI Y10.20.

The last example shown in Figure 2.3, that involving the bth root, illustrates a limited *vertical* positioning notation system that is also widely used, again due to Descartes. This notation involves the use of characters that are raised and smaller, called superscripts (above the written line), and their equivalent lowered symbols, called subscripts, as shown below:

$$A_c^b \text{ or } x_j^2$$

The convention most commonly used is that superscripts and subscripts are either lower case letters or numbers, and are placed immediately to the right of the object they refer to. Superscripts, often mean "raised to the power of…" or "raised to the exponent", and subscripts often mean "a member of…". In this context subscripts may be repeated or multiple, as in x_{ij},

Symbol type	Examples	Interpretation
Relational symbols	$\leq \geq \cong \equiv$	less than or equal to; greater than or equal to; approximately equal to (also $\approx$); equivalent to/congruent to
Set theory symbols	$\cup \cap \subseteq \notin$	union; intersection; partial or total subset; not a member of
Logic symbols	$\therefore \forall \because \exists$	therefore; for all members (upside down A); because; there exists (backwards facing E)
Fractions and roots	$\dfrac{a}{b} \quad a/b \quad \sqrt[b]{a}$	a divided by b; a divided by b; the bth root of a (e.g. the square root if $b=2$, or if b is omitted)

Figure 2.3 Selected symbols

but this usage is not consistent or universal. In right to left languages (and at the discretion of the writer) placement may be to the left of the object. The use of two or more subscripts is also frequently similar to the use of two or more variables in geometry to identify the location of a point along a line, on a plane, or in 3 dimensions. In the former case, however, it is used normally to indicate in which row, or row and column in a square or rectangular table or block of numbers the value is located. Thus x_{ij} means the value to be found in row i, column j. If there is only one row or column of numbers only one subscript is needed and the set $\{x_i\}$ is called a *vector*. Here the use of curly brackets $\{\}$ is taken to mean that the included entries are a well-defined collection of items (a set), in this case x_1, x_2, x_3 etc. With two subscripts the set $\{x_{ij}\}$ is called a *matrix*, and with more subscripts the term matrix is still used. The subscripts i,j etc. in such cases only take positive whole number (Integer) values: 1,2,3... etc.

Another widely used convention for subscripts is that if a dot or blob is shown where you would have expected a letter, then you assume that all possible values that can be ascribed to the letter are included — i.e. this is a form of shorthand to avoid the excessive use of additional symbols such as summation signs. Thus $\{x_i.\}$ typically means that the values have been added across the columns of a matrix, so this represents the vector of totals for each row; likewise, $\{x._j\}$ is the set of column totals and $\{x..\}$ is the grand total. Dots are also sometimes used directly above a symbol, with a variety of meanings (for example to indicate that number is a repeated decimal, as in:

$$0.3\dot{3}$$

In some instances, where a repeated decimal exhibits a repeating pattern of digits, as in 0.10891089... this is written with either two dots above (*overdots*), or a line above (a *vinculum*):

$$0.1\dot{0}8\dot{9} \text{ or } 0.\overline{1089}$$

If the object is an *operator* (i.e. a symbol that identifies a particular procedure or operation that is to be carried out) such as a Sum, Product or Integral symbol, then the sub- and super-script values indicate the lower and upper ranges to be used in the calculation. So, for example, the expression

$$\sum_{i=1}^{10} x_i$$

means find the sum of the x_i values for $i=1,2,3,...,10$, or $x_1+x_2+...+x_{10}$, and the expression

$$y_i = \sum_{j=1}^{4} w_{ij}x_{ij} \text{ for } i=1,2,3$$

means find the 3 sums $y_1=w_{11}x_{11}+w_{12}x_{12}+w_{13}x_{13}+w_{14}x_{14}$, $y_2=w_{21}x_{21}+...$, $y_3=w_{31}x_{31}+...$, where in this case the w's may be weights or constants and the y's and x's unknown values. So, for example, we might have

$$y_1 = 1x_{11} + 5x_{12} + 0x_{13} + 3x_{14}$$
$$y_2 = 2x_{21} + 0x_{22} + 7x_{23} + 1x_{24}$$
$$y_3 = 6x_{31} + 1x_{32} + 3x_{33} + 5x_{34}$$

In this case we can also regard the sums as a simple equation relating the y's to the x's (linear equations, since all the x's are to the power 1, there are no powers of 2, 3 etc.).

2.4 Blocks of numbers (matrices)

The notation in the last example is rather cumbersome and potentially confusing. One solution, which has many additional benefits and applications, is to focus on the weights or constants, and write these down as a block of numbers or symbols. In the example just given we have 3 rows of 4 values, which we can write in the form:

$$W = \begin{bmatrix} w_{11} & w_{12} & w_{13} & w_{14} \\ w_{21} & w_{22} & w_{23} & w_{24} \\ w_{31} & w_{32} & w_{33} & w_{34} \end{bmatrix} \text{ or } \begin{bmatrix} 1 & 5 & 0 & 3 \\ 2 & 0 & 7 & 1 \\ 6 & 1 & 3 & 5 \end{bmatrix}$$

This arrangement is called a *matrix*, in this case with 3 rows and 4 columns. The idea of working with blocks of numbers or expressions in this form dates from around 1855, so it is a relatively recent innovation in mathematics, although the fundamental ideas date back more than 2000 years to early Chinese and later Babylonian mathematics. If there is only 1 row or 1 column (or *dimension*) it tends to be called a *vector*. We generally only work with 1- or 2-dimensional matrices. If a square matrix (one with the same number of rows and columns) contains all zeros it is called the zero matrix (usually denoted **O**), and if it contains 1's along its diagonal (top left to bottom right) and zeros elsewhere, it is called a unit or Identity matrix (usually denoted **I** for identity). These two arrangements perform the functions of the numbers 0 and 1, but for matrix arithmetic. Capital letters, often in bold type, are used as an abbreviation for a matrix.

Over the last 150 years it has been found that working with matrices and vectors provides a very convenient and fast way of solving a large range of problems, from optimally cutting fabrics and carpets in a factory to modelling the workings of national economies, and from statistical data analysis to the solution of many problems in physics and astronomy. Part of the reason for their widespread usage is that they are very well-suited to a computational context, i.e. in the frameworks provided by modern computer systems and software.

I am not going to try and cover the ins and outs of matrices and matrix algebra here, but it is helpful to see some examples of their use, as these are so varied. The first example involves the analysis of chemical samples, whilst the second looks at finding the shortest route through a simplified road network (similar problems apply to telecommunications networks and electronic circuits). In Part II I take a look at their application in digital photography.

Our first example involves finding the solution to a question about grain harvests posed and solved by matrix-like methods in China around 300BC. I am going to re-express this as a modern-day pharmaceutical problem:

> A laboratory is provided with 3 samples in powder form that are claimed to be new headache remedies. The samples weigh 39, 34 and 26 grams respectively. Chemical analysis shows that the samples each contain a different mix of the same 3 ingredients: the first mix is in the proportions 3:2:1, the second is 2:3:1 and the last is 1:2:3. The lab needs to determine the actual amounts of each ingredient that have been used to create these 3 samples.

We can write this problem down using equations, calling the three unknown ingredient amounts x, y and z, as follows:

$$39 = 3x + 2y + z$$
$$34 = 2x + 3y + z$$
$$26 = x + 2y + 3z$$

In matrix notation this would be written as shown below, where the arrows indicate how the matrix multiplication process operates:

$$\begin{bmatrix} 39 \\ 34 \\ 26 \end{bmatrix} = \begin{bmatrix} 3 & 2 & 1 \\ 2 & 3 & 1 \\ 1 & 2 & 3 \end{bmatrix} \begin{bmatrix} x \\ y \\ z \end{bmatrix}$$

In this layout we can see that we have an arrangement of the form $b=Ax$ where b is a 3x1 column vector of numbers, A is a 3x3 matrix of numbers and x is a 3x1 column vector of unknowns containing the variables x, y and z that we wish to determine. The rules of multiplication are obviously a bit different from those we are used to. The basic idea is that each *row* of A multiplies the *column* of x and the results are added together, element by element. Thus row 1 of A times column 1 of x (there is only 1 column in this example) gives $3x+2y+z$. To do such multiplications the dimensions of the two matrices must be compatible, so that the number of columns in the first matrix must equal the number of rows in the second. In general $A \cdot B$ is not the same as $B \cdot A$, so the order of multiplication matters as well as the sizes of the matrices. In the first case ($A \cdot B$) we are *pre*-multiplying by A, in the second ($B \cdot A$) *post*-multiplying by A.

Now, the arrangement above is of the form $b=Ax$, so it would be great if we could re-arrange this by 'dividing' both sides by A to give $b/A=x$ thus solving our problem for x, i.e. the 3 unknown elements x, y and z. In matrix algebra the equivalent to division is called *inversion* and the inverse of A is written A^{-1}. We can then pre-multiply both sides of $b=Ax$ by A^{-1} to give:

$A^{-1}b=A^{-1}Ax$ or $A^{-1}b=x$ (since $A^{-1}A=I$ and $Ix=x$)

We do need to check that the calculation of A^{-1} is possible and does not give us the equivalent of dividing by zero, but here we will assume that the operation is safe! You can compute A^{-1} using Maple, MATLab or Excel (using its built-in function Minverse()). To save time here I will simply write the answer down, as given by Maple (i.e. as fractions rather than decimals):

$$A^{-1} = \begin{bmatrix} +\dfrac{7}{12} & -\dfrac{1}{3} & -\dfrac{1}{12} \\ -\dfrac{5}{12} & +\dfrac{2}{3} & -\dfrac{1}{12} \\ +\dfrac{1}{12} & -\dfrac{1}{3} & +\dfrac{5}{12} \end{bmatrix}$$

Now we can compute $A^{-1}b$ and we find $x=37/4$, $y=17/4$ and $z=11/4$. If you put these values back into the original equations you will see that these are the correct amounts of each ingredient in the samples supplied to the lab.

In general, if we have two matrices $A_{p,q}$ and $B_{q,r}$ where p, q and r are the sizes of the matrices (in rows, columns order) then it is valid to calculate $C=A*B$ and the result will be $C_{p,r}$. So the dimensions rule is that the inner dimensions must match: $(p,q)\times(q,r)$ gives a result of dimension (p,r). A simple example serves to illustrate the process, in this case a 2x2 matrix times a 2x1 matrix, giving a 2x1 matrix:

$$\begin{bmatrix} a & b \\ c & d \end{bmatrix} \times \begin{bmatrix} e \\ f \end{bmatrix} = \begin{bmatrix} a*e+b*f \\ c*e+d*f \end{bmatrix}$$

If $p=r=1$ we have two matrices which consist of 1 row for A and 1 column for B (thus both are vectors). For example, in the multiplication below with $q=3$, we have the dimensions $(1,3)\times(3,1)=(1,1)$:

$$\begin{bmatrix} 4 & 5 & 6 \end{bmatrix} \begin{bmatrix} 9 \\ 8 \\ 7 \end{bmatrix} = 4*9+5*8+6*7 = 36+40+42 = 118$$

So when two *vectors* are multiplied in this way the result is a single value (a 1x1 matrix or *scalar*). This result will be used in Part II in our discussion of smarter ways to divide and multiply numbers. A row vector, such as $v=[4,5,6]$ or $v=[3.4,0.4,12.5]$ can also be seen as a point in 3-dimensional space (see Figure 2.4). This form of representation of space using a box-like arrangement of straight lines at right angles to each other (*axes*) is another convention introduced by Descartes,

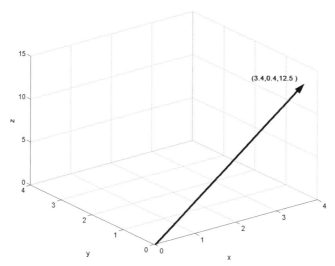

Figure 2.4 3D representation of a vector

and for this reason it is known as *Cartesian*.

If we represent our 3 element vector, *v*, as an arrow extending from the point [0,0,0] to [3.4,0.4,12.5] then we often need to know the *magnitude* or size (length) of this vector. We can obtain this number very simply by evaluating the product $v*v^T$ where v^T is the vector *v* arranged as a column (this arrangement is called the *transform* of *v*, for which the superscript T is used). This gives us a single value that is the sum of the squares of the elements of *v*. In our 3-space example we find: $v*v^T=3.4^2+0.4^2+12.5^2=167.97$ thus $|v|=\sqrt{167.97}=12.96$, where the vertical lines in $|v|$ indicate that we are showing the size (length) of the vector. So we can think of a vector in an additional way, as an object like an arrow, with a direction and a magnitude. This is often useful for problems involving variables of this kind, as in modelling fluid flows and in the study of electromagnetic and gravitational phenomena.

A simple example of the use of vectors is in the representation of the colours used in digital images. Typically, coloured digital images are stored as a set of values of picture elements, or pixels, in row and column (matrix) format. So an image that is 500x500 pixels would contain a number or set of numbers associated with every pixel identifying the colour of that pixel. The colour information is often stored as three elements: Red, Green and Blue, each of which may have 256 values (2^8 or 8 bits, i.e. 1 byte) from 0 to 255. (0,0,0) is then Black, (255,0,0) is Red, (0,255,0) is Green, (0,0,255) is Blue, and (255,255,255) is White. All other colours are a mix of the three RGB components, giving a total of $(2^8)^3=2^{24}$ colours, or 16.8 million, all stored in 3 bytes per pixel. These arrangements can be conveniently represented as vectors in 3D space (or *colour space* in this case), as shown in Figure 2.5. In Part II I show how you can use these forms of image representation to manipulate digital images. For our 500x500 picture we need 750,000

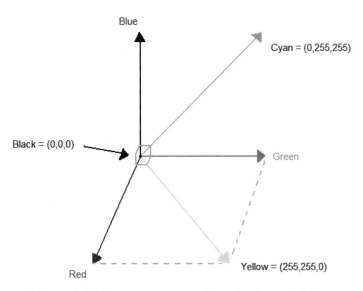

Figure 2.5 Vector representation of colours in 3D space

(500x500x3) bytes for storage, assuming no compression. But with most images, compression using coding schemes such as JPEG or GIF are the norm, so far less space is required on digital photocards and computer disks.

A rather different example involves using matrices to represent the structure of a road network, shown in Figure 2.6. In this case each entry in the matrix provides information on the road links — if two places are linked they are given a value of 1, or a value of 0 to indicate that they are

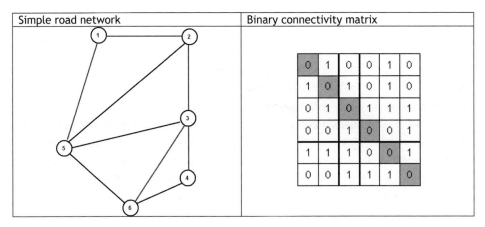

Figure 2.6 Graph and matrix representation of a road network

not directly connected (places are not regarded as linked to themselves, so the diagonal entries are all set to 0). In this case the rows indicate *From* and the columns indicate *To*. Because there are no one-way streets shown the connectivity matrix is symmetric — its upper and lower sections either side of the diagonal from top left (shown shaded) are mirror images of each other. We are going to use this representation to identify the shortest paths through a road network.

Let us denote the binary connectivity matrix by the letter **C** and calculate $C^2 = C*C$ (take my word for it, this is useful). First we multiply row 1 by column 1 to get cell position $c_{11} = 0*0 + 1*1 + 0*0 + 0*0 + 1*1 + 0*0 = 2$. This gives us the number of ways in which we can leave location 1 and get back to it in 2 steps — which can be confirmed from the diagram (from $1 \to 2 \to 1$ and $1 \to 5 \to 1$). Now we calculate the next cell entry in the same way, row 1 column 2, or $c_{12} = 0*1 + 1*0 + 0*1 + 0*0 + 1*1 + 0*0 = 1$, so there is just 1 way of getting from location 1 to location 2 in two steps — this is the route from 1 to 5 to 2. More generally, if we compute the whole of C^2 we get a matrix showing all the possible two-step routes from every location to every other one. Likewise, from C^3 we get all 3-step routes and we can continue this process until there are no cells in C^n that contain 0's. This occurs when every point is reached from every other point, and is called the *diameter* of the network (or sometimes the solution time).

Instead of doing all this by hand, you can perform these multiplications very simply in Maple or MATLab, and it is also fairly easy to get Excel to generate these results (using its Mmult() function). The results are shown below:

C¹

0	1	0	0	1	0
1	0	1	0	1	0
0	1	0	1	1	1
0	0	1	0	0	1
1	1	1	0	0	1
0	0	1	1	1	0

C²

2	1	2	0	1	1
1	3	1	1	2	2
2	1	4	1	2	2
0	1	1	2	2	1
1	2	2	2	4	1
1	2	2	1	1	3

C³

2	5	3	3	6	3
5	4	8	3	7	4
3	8	6	6	9	7
3	3	6	2	3	5
6	7	9	3	6	8
3	4	7	5	8	4

By the time 3-steps links have been made all the cells contain non-zero values, so the diameter of the network is 3 and we stop there. In these matrices I have shaded some of the cells — they are shaded if they contain a value >0 having had a 0 entry in the previous matrix. These identify the length (in terms of steps) of the shortest paths from any location to any other. For example, consider the set of routes from location 1 in our original diagram. There are 3 different ways in which the route from location 1 to location 4 can be achieved (1-2-3-4, 1-5-3-4 and 1-5-6-4) and this is indicated by the number 3 in the cell of C^3 that has been shaded. But that's more than enough about matrices for the time being. I will return to their use in Part II.

2.5   Punctuation

In the case of computers, the important thing is to store numbers in as precise, consistent and meaningful format as is possible with the available technology. We then need to convert this information into alternative forms for processing, display or output according to a set of rules that apply for the country and/or data type in question. Most of us are familiar with this problem in the context of the formats that other countries use for dates, times, telephone numbers and currencies. Less familiar are country-specific number-handling rules.

A simple example serves to illustrate some of the problems — the mysterious comma. In the quote shown below, from the delightful book by Lynn Truss on punctuation in English, the meaning of the phrase

"Eats shoots and leaves"

is entirely changed if a comma is included after the word "Eats". With a comma after "Eats" we might be describing a lone gunfighter, entering a bar for a meal, shooting a customer and exiting rapidly. Without a comma added we could be describing a Panda.

In the context of numbers, commas have an equally vital role, and are often used to break long numbers into three digit subsets (thousands). For example:

12456789.00 can be written as 12,456,789.00

for greater clarity. Occasionally, but not in North America, 12456789.00 is written as 12456789·00, i.e. using a raised or 'middle' dot. However in many countries, including much of Europe, the use of the period (raised or otherwise) is not acceptable since commas are used in preference to decimal point notation and the 'correct' format is:

12456789,00 which may also be written as 12 456 789,00

The risk, in this second example, is that digits can be inserted into the gaps, which invites forgery, so for many financial institutions (banks etc.) such an arrangement is unsatisfactory. It is however officially permitted in Belgium, Luxemburg and French-speaking Canada.

By contrast, in India only the first block of a thousand is separated by a comma. After this commas are used to separate hundreds, as in:

12456789.00 which may be written as 1,24,56,789.00

Very large numbers, such as those with perhaps 20 or more digits, which are important in applications such as data security, are often written with blocks of 5 digits separated by commas or spaces.

Such differences matter a great deal, since not only can they lead to confusion when you read them, but they may result in incorrect processing of numbers. For example, a widely used data exchange format is the readable text arrangement known as Comma Separated Value (CSV) files. But if commas form part of the format of an individual number, this data format may produce files that are completely incorrect. To solve this difficulty a CSV file for use in France, say, typically uses a semi-colon (;) to separate the numbers rather than a comma. In countries that use a right-to-left mode of writing, commas are reversed, hence in Arabic:

, becomes '

Other punctuation symbols are used in a wide range of contexts, but rarely with consistent or universal meaning. The exclamation mark, written in its standard form as !, is used to denote a factorial operation (as noted earlier), i.e.

$n!=n(n-1)(n-2)...1$
e.g. $4!=4*3*2*1$

Quotation marks "" and ''; brackets ( ), { }, [ ]; and spaces are widely used to separate and group numbers and expressions, but there is much scope for confusion and error. For example, when $<a,b>$ is used does it refer to a form of bracketing, or arithmetic operations of greater than and less than, or perhaps some other operation such as assignment? Likewise, the use of square brackets, such as [0,5] is often used to mean "numbers in the range 0 to 5, *including* the values 0 and 5" (generally called the *closed* interval), whilst (0,5) may refer to the same range but *excluding* 0 and 5 (generally called the *open* interval), or may mean simply the pair of values 0 and 5.

As far as possible, most computer software packages, particularly those that are designed for symbolic analysis, will attempt to identify and report on such issues from the context in which the user is working, but there is no guarantee that this interpretation will be correct or unique. In the case of the use of brackets, it is essential to check that every opened bracket has a corresponding closing bracket, and to recognise that nested brackets, i.e. bracketed expressions within other brackets, are normally to be calculated from the inside outwards and from left to right. So, $(a*(b*(c-2)))$ is calculated as $c-2$ (=R1 say), then $b*R1$ (=R2 say), and finally as $a*R2$. It is also important to observe that bracketing is only a valid operation for finite series — with infinite series it may give incorrect results.

Bracketing focuses attention on rules of precedence, i.e. rules relating to the order in which operations will be carried out. Mathematical expressions entered into computer programs are

-	Negation (as in -1)
%	Percent
^	Exponentiation
* and /	Multiplication and division
+ and -	Addition and subtraction
= < > <= >= <>	Comparison

Figure 2.7 Excel precedence rules

processed according to well-defined rules of precedence. These rules will vary according to the particular software involved, but typically operations are evaluated from left to right, with bracketing over-riding other rules, as described above. The precedence rules for basic mathematical operations in many software packages are similar, and are as shown in Figure 2.7 (these are Excel's rules, highest precedence first).

Because there is a very limited subset of easily typed characters (letters, numbers and sundry symbols) on most computer systems, these characters are used and re-used in many different ways. As we noted earlier, the widespread use of the ASCII 8-bit coding scheme means that at most 255 distinct letters, numbers and symbols are available. To extend this set an alternative coding system using more than 8 bits is required or symbols must be used in combination. For example the combination := may be used as a single operator, meaning *assignment*, such that the left hand side of the expression is assigned the value or expression on the right hand side. This is differentiated from = meaning *equality*, such that the two sides of the expression have the same value. Entering more complex expressions and symbol arrangements into computer systems requires additional facilities in the software one uses. This subject is covered in more detail in Part II.

2.6 Rounding

"When completing your personal tax return please do not use pence. Round down your income and gains. Round up your tax credits and tax deductions. Round to the nearest pound." UK Inland Revenue Income Tax form guidance, 2004

Rounding numbers up or down is a source of constant difficulties. In most countries the norm in basic arithmetic operations is to round decimal numbers that end in 0...4 down, and numbers that end in 5...9 up. For example, 12.045 would be rounded up to 12.05 whilst 12.044 would be rounded down to 12.04. This rule favours rounding up, since a number ending in 0 does not strictly speaking require rounding. An alternative, used as the default in some software packages (such as Maple), is to round to the nearest whole number, with ties being rounded to the nearest *even* value. To illustrate this, we can set the maximum number of digits to be handled to just 2 and then look at an expression like 1.25x2. The software will change the value 1.25 to 1.2, because it rounds to the nearest even value in the case of a tie (it could go up or down in this case), and instead of producing the correct answer 2.5, it calculates the result as 2.4; had we chosen the expression 1.35x2 then answer given would have been 2.8. In practice you may not observe this effect unless you are working with large numbers, because the default number of digits used by the package in question is 10, so it will look absolutely correct in most instances. But the principle remains the same — rounding numbers alters results.

A good example is exam marking. In Table 2-2 we see the marks awarded to two students for 4 exam questions. Each question has been marked out of 50, and the average of the examiners' marks used to score each question, with halves being rounded up. Student 1 is awarded 71% for her exam paper whilst Student 2 receives 70%, despite the fact that Student 2 actually scored more on the paper than Student 1, as can be seen from the totals.

Rounding can be a significant problem where multiple computations are involved, because small effects can be greatly exaggerated. For example, if a number like 1.124 is treated as if it were really 1.12, and we need to evaluate 1.124^{10} (which is 1.124*1.124*...1.124, 10 times), we would find the answer in the first case being 3.219 (rounded to 3 decimal places, or *dp*) whereas the second case would give us an answer of 3.11 (in this case rounded to 2dp). Simple examples like this are not likely to occur with modern computers, but in more complex expressions and with numbers involving more digits (not necessary large numbers) the errors can be substantial or even catastrophic (i.e. completely incorrect). Take for example the following expression:

$$\frac{1335}{4}b^6 + a^2\left(11a^2b^2 - b^6 - 121b^4 - 2\right) + \frac{11}{2}b^8 + \frac{a}{2b}$$

Let us put this expression into a Microsoft Excel spreadsheet, with cell B1=77617 as *a* and cell B2=33096 as *b*. The symbol ^ is used in Excel for "raised to the power of", so the expression is something like:

=1335/4*B2^6+B1^2*(11*B1^2*B2^2-B2^6-121*B2^4-2)+11/2*B2^8+B1/(2*B2)

Table 2-2 Rounding exam marks

Question number	1	1	2	2	3	3	4	4	%	Total marks
Examiner	a	b	a	b	a	b	a	b		
Student 1										
Mark given	23	22	30	41	34	33	45	50		278
Rounded average		23		36		34		48	71%	
Student 2										
Mark given	23	23	31	41	33	33	46	50		280
Rounded average		23		36		33		48	70%	

Excel gives the answer as -1.18059E+21 (E here means 'exponent with base10', i.e. -1.18059x10^{21}) a very large negative number. The correct answer is -0.827..., which shows how wrong computations can be when certain types of calculation are required!

This is a particularly testing example, designed to check how well computers deal with rounding, so I will look at it again a bit later on (see Part II and Appendix 1). Here is what Microsoft's current advice for software developers says on number precision:

> *The float [single precision] type can represent values ranging from approximately* *1.5x10^{-45} to 3.4x10^{38}* **with a precision of 7 digits.** *The double type can represent* *values ranging from approximately 5.0x10^{-324} to 1.7x10^{308}* **with a precision of 15-16** **digits.**

So, despite the fact that very large numbers can be handled, the precision of numbers is only 15 or 16 decimal digits at best, with consequent risk of rounding and related errors, as we have just seen. Essentially there are two kinds of problem here:

(i)   roundoff errors — rounding off numbers and computations due to the way in which the rules are applied and/or the computer performs basic operations such as addition, subtraction, multiplication and division; and
(ii)   representation errors — where numbers are not stored precisely because they cannot be adequately represented in the computer. Together these errors are called rounding or truncation errors.

Most taxation authorities, banks and similar financial institutions have very well defined rules on the handling of rounding, since with computations such as the calculation of interest and commission payments on very large amounts, there is plenty of scope for rounded sums to accumulate or 'go missing'. Furthermore, some countries including Argentina, Canada and Switzerland have rules governing the rounding of currency values that are more complicated than simple rounding up or down. Thus in Switzerland rounding is carried out to the nearest 5 cents rather than 1 cent, so all values in the range 3.176 SFr to 3.225 SFr must be rounded to 3.20 SFr.

Many modern computer software packages provide specific functions for various forms of rounding. For example, the Int() function is provided in many packages (includes Excel and most variants of Basic), to mean take the Integer part of a number. So Int(3.4)=3. But Int(-3.4)=-4, i.e. this function rounds to the nearest Integer below the current value. Several software implementations call this the Floor() function. They may also provide a Ceiling() function, which rounds up to the nearest Integer greater than the current value, thus Ceiling(-3.4)=-3 and Ceiling(3.4)=4. To complete the main set of such operations, the function Round() does precisely that, rounding a number to the nearest Integer value, so Round(-3.4)=-3 and Round(3.4)=3.

2.7   Padding

In our discussion of decimals and in currency representation I noted that there are parts of a number that may need to be written explicitly with a certain number of digits and no spaces. It is common practice to pad out a number that has fewer digits than the maximum with leading zeros, for example, writing 9 cents as 09 cents, or the year 2004 as 04. In general numbers are not written with leading zeros and many software packages will strip off any leading zeros unless you declare the information as being 'text' rather than numeric.

Retention of leading zeros can be very useful. Consider the set of numbers {1,2,3,10,11}. If we sort these into ascending order on a computer the result will depend on whether they are recognised and processed as a set of numbers or as text. For example, if these were file names (or the start or end of filenames) they would be sorted into the sequence {1,10,11,2,3}. This would not occur if the values were zero padded, as {01,02,03,10,11}.

2.8   Precision and accuracy

The rounding of numbers, such as fractional parts of currencies, is a small member of a much larger family of issues. It is extremely important that these are more widely understood, and do not remain simply as facts that are familiar within the realm of software engineers.

2.8.1 Precision

Unfortunately the term precision is used to mean different things in different scientific disciplines. It is widely used in an engineering context to mean a process or device that generates results which may be reproduced to a pre-specified fine degree of tolerance or exactness. The second main usage, which we will focus upon, is in the field of digital systems (computers and related equipment and software). Precision in this case refers to the number of meaningful or *significant* digits stored and/or displayed. Within computer systems precision is often taken to mean the largest number that the computer can store exactly. This number will be a positive Integer (whole number, e.g. 65535) and is normally determined by the physical hardware of the computer and the way in which its operating system utilises the hardware. For example, until the 1980s, almost all but the largest and most expensive computers were based on 16 bit processors. The largest number that can be stored in 2 bits is decimal 3, this being the binary number 11. With 3 bits we have 111, which is 7 in decimal, or 2^3-1. With 16 bits the largest (unsigned) number that can be stored is $2^{16}-1=65535$. This is not a very large number at all, so computers were programmed to enable the software to combine blocks of 16 bits into larger units, in order to offer greater precision for arithmetic operations. Of course this procedure is much slower and more cumbersome than relying on the hardware to do the job, and very soon the standard hardware base moved to 32 bit computers, enabling numbers up to roughly 4000 million to be stored exactly. By working with so-called "double precision", 64 bit numbers could be handled, which means numbers with up to 20 decimal digits. In the last couple of years 64-bit processors have become available for low cost computers, such as those built on Intel chipsets. With double precision these processors will support numbers up to 38 decimal digits.

When computer magazines and promotional material talk about "1k" or "1meg" or "1gig" they do not mean one thousand, one million or a thousand million. They mean the power of 2 that is slightly greater than these values. So 1k means $2^{10}=1024$, 1meg means $2^{20}=1,048,576$ and 1gig means $2^{30}=1,073,741,824$. Actually it is a bit more complicated than this. The reason is that usually these terms refer to "bytes", which are collections of 8 bits, because a great deal of data and text is stored in a coded form (such as ASCII) that uses 8 bits to identify the different symbols (letters, numbers etc.) needed for display. So "1k" storage generally means 1 kilobyte or 8192 bits, but a dial-up communication link described as "48k" typically means 48 kilobits/second maximum transmission speed (i.e. roughly 6kbytes/second).

Precision that is provided in software rather than hardware is sometimes referred to as *arbitrary precision*, since it can support levels of precision that are not dependent on the underlying hardware. In addition, there are computing environments which do not use the concept of fixed precision at all, since they aim to provide *exact computation*: by providing any number of digits as requested by the user; or by using as many digits as are required for a particular part of a problem (multi-precision computation); or by expressing output in symbolic form where a finite number of digits is not appropriate or acceptable.

Precision is not the same as accuracy, because accuracy relates to the quality of specific measurements or computations, irrespective of the precision of the systems used. To make this clearer, we now define accuracy, which is a somewhat subtler concept.

2.8.2 Accuracy
Accuracy is broadly defined as "the closeness of observations to true values or values accepted to be true". In other words our notion of accuracy depends on the quality of some measurement process and our acceptance of the results. So we might describe a watch as "very accurate" if it keeps time to within a minute over a period of a year compared to a reference clock such as the GMT time signal. Or we might describe a series of measurements of the position of the Moon as having a high degree of accuracy, and then go on to describe the range of values found. A narrow range of observations, especially where many observations are taken and are found to be in close agreement, gives us cause to suggest that the measurements are very accurate — in fact, such results might show a consistent error or bias, for example if the equipment used contained some alignment error.

Accuracy of numbers is more complex than these comments suggest. For a start it is likely that the numbers represent something in the real world, for example the height of a building, the weight of a set of ingredients, the area of a plot of land. By assigning a number to these real-world objects we are implicitly assuming that there is some model for height, weight, surface area etc. that uniquely translates these verbal descriptions and the real-world observations into abstract numbers (if this seems an odd idea, see the discussion on dimensionality, Section 7). Second, we assume that if we measure something we will obtain a single value, which is almost never the case — repeated measurement nearly always results in a series of values, whose variation depends on the person or persons doing the measurement, the equipment being used, environmental conditions such as temperature and humidity, and many other factors. If we are using a single value it normally indicates that we have either only made one measurement or are taking the average of a set of measurements as our best estimate of the 'true' value. Much of the discipline of statistics is concerned with this specific problem, and how to minimise such variations and/or isolate known factors that may distort or explain the results we record.

A further issue is time. Many measurements are made at a specific time, and measurements taken at a different time or over a long period of time may yield different values. For example, if you measure the amount of moisture in 10 samples in a small plot of soil, the average value might be an excellent estimate of the moisture for the plot as a whole. But if the measurement was repeated at a different time of day, or under different humidity or seasonal conditions, the results may be quite different. Such questions can be described as issues of temporal variation. *Temporal accuracy* is the term used to describe the relationship between the time at which the measurement was made and the time, if any, that is recorded for this measurement. Note that where measurements are stored in a computer, the date and time stamp on the item's record is rarely the date and time of the measurement — it is typically the time it was placed on the computer. Likewise, such dates and times do not provide an indication of how current or valid the numbers are. Ideally there should be additional data (known as *metadata*) stored on the computer providing details on the date(s) and time(s) of data gathering.

A final issue is what is known as *thematic accuracy*. This term is used to refer to a variety of issues, an example of which is whether the information provided has been correctly classified. For example, we may be told that the number of thefts *from* vehicles in a particular district over the last year was 1217 and the number of thefts *of* vehicles over the same period was 807. However, mis-recording may have resulted in some thefts *from* vehicles being recorded as *of* vehicles, and vice versa.

2.9 Exponents, logarithms and magnitude

2.9.1 Exponential notation

When numbers are too large or too small to represent conveniently with a string of digits, a notation known as "exponential", "standard" or "scientific" form is often utilised. This represents numbers using three elements: a single digit before the decimal point (sometimes known as the *characteristic*); a variable number of digits after the decimal point (known as the fractional part or *mantissa*, especially where the number is a logarithmic value — see later in this section); and a scale factor in the same base. For example, 345.678 would be written as 3.45678E+2 (although occasionally it is written as 0.345678E+3). The E+2 (or E+3) indicates that the number needs to be multiplied by an exponent of +2 (or +3), with base10 in this example (this is the normal form of representation) i.e. 10^2 (or 10^3). Multiples of 10 are sometimes referred to as "orders of magnitude". Exponential notation is not reserved for base10 numbers only, and when seen or used the relevant base should be specified or clear from the context. Note that $10^1=10$, and this is true for any base, x. So, for example $12^1=12$, $1.768^1=1.768$ etc. Furthermore, $10^0=1$, $12^0=1$ and $1.768^0=1$ and you can easily confirm that $x^0=1$ for all $x\neq0$ using Excel.

Addition and subtraction of numbers in exponential form is simplest to perform if the values are modified so that the exponents have the same value. For example, 3.45E+6 + 8.98E+2 is straight-forward if we rewrite this (by moving the decimal point for the first number by 4 positions to the right) as 34500.0E+2 + 8.98E+2 giving 34508.98E+2. The same procedure works for subtraction and for negative exponents. Multiplication and division involve addition and subtraction of the exponent parts and multiplication or division of the numbers. So 3.45E+6x8.98E+2= (3.45x8.98)E+(2+6)=30.981E+8 or 3.0981E+9. Of course, calculators and computers handle these processes internally and then display the appropriate answer for you, but it's a good idea to know how the procedure works in order to be able to check that the answer looks correct (after all, we have already seen how badly wrong Excel can be).

Exponents do not have to be Integers or zero. For example, consider the number $1.414...=\sqrt{2}=2^{1/2}$ or $2^{0.5}$. Just as any number may be written in scientific notation, so any number can be expressed as a (fractional) power of a base, such as 2 or 10. If we consider the number 2 using 10 as a base for the exponent, we have $2=10^x$, where x is some fraction to be determined. There are several ways of deciding what value x should have, but for the moment we shall use our (inefficient but simple) binary chop procedure (a better procedure, using a series, is described in Part II). We know that $10^1=10$ and $10^0=1$, so we could start with these as our upper and lower ranges, iterating until eventually we find x. Trying x=0.5 we obtain 3.162... (e.g. using the Excel expression =10^0.5) which is too high, so we try x=0.25 giving 1.7782 (too low) until eventually we find x=0.30103... giving 2.000... (to a sufficient approximation) thus $2=10^{0.3010}...$. The three dot symbol ... at the end of these numbers indicates that the sequence continues indefinitely (with or without repetition) and is known as an *ellipsis*. Likewise, we would find $3=10^{0.4771}...$. Now, since we *add* exponents to perform multiplication it follows that $2*3=6=10^{(0.3010+0.4771...)}$, i.e. $6=10^{(0.7781...)}$ and $6*6=36=10^{(1.5562...)}$ obtained simply by adding the exponents.

2.9.2 Logarithms and Bones
The exponents in the examples above are called Common or base10 logarithms, and usually are written as log(36)=1.5562... This process reduces multiplication to addition, which is far simpler (especially by hand), assuming that we have tables of values for all numbers we are likely to need. Such tables were produced in 1614 by Scotsman John Napier (but not using base10) and then in 1624 by an associate, Henry Briggs, the latter using base10. These were in widespread usage until recent times.

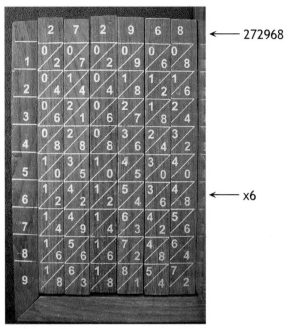

272968

x6

Figure 2.8 Set of modern Napier "Bones"

Napier was more widely known in his lifetime and for many years after his death for his introduction of 'bones', a form of physical multiplication tables (Figure 2.8). In this example the bones are being used to calculate 272968 times 6 (see the arrows which identify the number to be multiplied and the row to use).

Napiers 'bones' are sets of sticks (sometimes made of bone or ivory) one of which (or the frame of a board) is marked with the numbers 1,2,...9 from top to bottom. The others (of which there may be several copies) include a single number 0,1,2,...9 at the top and the results of multiplying this number by 1,2,...9 down their length. So on the stick with 2 at its top, we would find the numbers 2,4,6,8,10,12 etc. down its length, from 2x2, 2x3, 2x4 etc. The sticks can then be arranged side by side so that multiplying 272968x6 for example (as shown in this picture) can be done by reading off the answer for 6x2=12, 6x7=42 etc. which are already engraved on the sticks, and then adding up the results. This process is illustrated in the diagram below:

	2	7	2	9	6	8
6	1/2	4/2	1/2	5/4	3/6	4/8
	1 6	3	7	8	0	8

To get the final answer you add across the diagonals to obtain the lower (shaded) result, starting at the right hand end (i.e. 8, then 4+6=10, so retain the 0 and carry the 1 onto the 3), giving 1637808. These 'bones' were widely used until well into the 20th century.

2.9.3 Magnitude

Although exponential notation allows numbers of almost any size to be written down in a compact form, it may or may not provide a precise representation of the underlying number, depending upon the precision of the computer (the number of digits it can handle) and the nature of the number being displayed. Furthermore, whilst exponential notation is very convenient, it is also quite easy to make huge mistakes — confusing results in millimetres and metres for example. As a general rule, whenever working with numbers, take time to look critically at the results. A first check should be to see if they appear to be the right size, or *magnitude* (sometimes described as an order of *magnitude* check). Also it is important to check whether the units in which they are quoted make sense/correspond to your expectations. If in doubt, either re-work the sum or try working backwards from the answer to the original figures, or try using another method or system to calculate the result.

Checking magnitudes can provide interesting new insights into a problem. Here is a quick example:

"Mammals have distinctive two-part hearts that beat regularly to pump blood around their bodies. Elephants, weighing several tons, have hearts that beat around 30 times per minute and they live for around 50 years. Humans (in the West) have an average lifespan of around 70 years and their typical heart rate is about 70 times per minute. Mice and similar small rodents typically live for only 3 years but their hearts beat about 10 times faster then humans. Canaries and hummingbirds (like many other small birds) have around 800-1000 heartbeats per minute and live for 5-6 years. Ostriches have heart rates and lifespans similar to humans."

Can we draw any broad conclusions from this information?

We start by noting that there are roughly $S=60 \times 24 \times 365 \approx 0.5 \times 10^6$ minutes in a year. An order of magnitude analysis of the number of heartbeats in an average lifetime shows:

Elephants: $3 \times 10^1 \times 5 \times 10^1 \times S = 0.5 \times 15 \times 10^8 \approx 1 \times 10^9$
Humans: $7 \times 10^1 \times 7 \times 10^1 \times S = 0.5 \times 49 \times 10^8 \approx 2.5 \times 10^9$
Small mammals: $7 \times 10^2 \times 3 \times S = 0.5 \times 21 \times 10^8 \approx 1 \times 10^9$
Small Birds: $1 \times 10^3 \times 6 \times S = 0.5 \times 6 \times 10^9 \approx 3 \times 10^9$

From this simple analysis we conclude that it appears that many mammals live for around a billion heartbeats, although humans and birds seem to have a longer lifespan than one might otherwise expect. It has been suggested that humans may have a longer life expectancy because of the relatively large brain capacity, but ostriches, whose brains are smaller than their eyes, would seem to be a pretty convincing counter example!

Table 2-3 SI prefixes

Factor	Prefix	Symbol	Factor	Prefix	Symbol
10^{18}	exa	E	10^{-1}	deci	d
10^{15}	peta	P	10^{-2}	centi	c
10^{12}	tera	T	10^{-3}	milli	m
10^{9}	giga	G	10^{-6}	micro	μ
10^{6}	mega	M	10^{-9}	nano	n
10^{3}	kilo	k	10^{-12}	pico	p
10^{2}	hecto	h	10^{-15}	femto	f
10^{1}	deka	da	10^{-18}	atto	a

There is an agreed international standard (SI, or Système Internationale) terminology for orders of magnitude and the use of exponential notation using base10 powers. This terminology is summarised in Table 2-3, and shows the set of prefixes and symbols that should be used. There is one exception, the kilogram, for which the prefix is not used since the name of the standard unit already includes the relevant prefix (kilo).

2.10 Data granularity and resolution

These terms refer to the degree to which objects can be regarded as distinct or separate. When we talk about an apple, we know we are referring to a single, entire object, not a basket of apples, or the component parts of an apple. But frequently it is not quite as clear as this. For example, in the UK a full 7-digit postcode (or ZIP code in the USA) does not identify a single property, but a collection of perhaps 10-15 properties. It is given a single (unique) national grid reference, but refers to a set of items (a list of addresses) in the neighbourhood of this point. Likewise, the UK census districts for 2001 are based on collections of areas determined by 7-digit postcodes, and the smallest unit of data available (designed to ensure data anonymity) is 20 or so such areas combined. On many occasions the data one is using has a specific level of detail, which is either implicit or explicitly stated. This is what I mean by *granularity*. In some instances it may be possible to obtain data that has more detail or better (finer) granularity. For example, much information is grouped or classified by subject. Finer granularity may be achieved by increasing the detail associated with the classification method. Other examples of data granularity or resolution include: deliberately modified data, designed to ensure that individuals or events are not precisely identifiable (e.g. crime data records, census records); Global Positioning Satellite (GPS) location information before May 2000 (until this date civilian use of this data was deliberately altered by the US military to be accurate to only 100 metres instead of 10 metres); subsea mapping data (generally only available for commercial use at a resolution of several hundred metres); and image resolution in digital photography, satellite monitoring and scanning processes.

3 MEASUREMENT

"Pure logical thinking cannot yield us any knowledge of the empirical world; all knowledge of reality starts from experience and ends in it... experience is the alpha and the omega of all our knowledge of reality." A Einstein, 1933, Spencer Lecture "On the method of theoretical physics"

In the early part of the 18th century one of the hottest topics in science was whether the Earth was truly spherical or not. English scientists, led by Sir Isaac Newton and Edmond Halley, insisted that it was a bit flatter at the poles (oblate, like a grapefruit) whilst French astronomers, led by J J Cassini, disagreed and believed it was slightly pointed (prolate, rather like a lemon). Knowing the size and shape of the Earth was to prove of great importance, and formed the foundation stone of much research by French scientists throughout the century. A landmark project in this programme took place in the years 1736-8. The French Academie des Sciences sent two teams to measure parts of the Earth's surface North and South of the equator. The team heading North were led by Pierre-Louis Moreau de Maupertius. He went to the Arctic Circle (66 degrees North) in modern-day Finland, and established a carefully measured baseline of 8.9 miles on the frozen river Torne (Tornea).

Using a frozen surface ensured that the line measured was extremely close to being level and smooth. This work, coupled with detailed astronomical observations, enabled the length of a degree of latitude (i.e. a North-South arc) to be estimated at the Arctic Circle. His measurements proved conclusively that the Earth was oblate (flattened at the poles) rather than prolate. A second team were sent to Peru (near Quito, in Ecuador today) to perform similar measurements (1735-1743), which together with the findings from Finland led to the first modern definition of the Earth's shape, in 1743, as a squashed sphere or *ellipsoid*. This shape has a semi-major axis (effectively the radius at the equator) of 6,397,300metres (i.e. around 6400 kilometres) and flattening factor: 1/216.8, or about 0.5%, quite close to the values we use today.

3.1   The size of things

Following somewhat in the footsteps of Maupertius, early in the winter of 1744 on a bright cold morning, an ambitious young schoolmaster named Murdoch MacKenzie stepped onto the frozen surface of a small lake close to his home. The lake in question was the Loch of Stenhouse and is situated on the largest of the Orkney Islands, off the north coast of the Scottish mainland. This event marked the start of a very significant but little known development in our understanding of coastlines. Like Maupertius, Mackenzie was embarking upon a lengthy programme of very careful measurements.

MacKenzie's endeavour was an opportunist, private venture, funded by subscriptions from the Hudson Bay Company, London merchants, insurance businesses, friends and wealthy patrons. As such, it was a very 'modern' plan, and we can imagine similar ideas being proposed and considered today. It was to take him four years to complete, make his name and a reasonable fortune, and ultimately gain him election to the Royal Society.

Onto the ice he dragged a box containing a long metal chain, many lengths of rope and a large number of wooden poles. He made a smooth hole in the ice and inserted the end of one of the poles as his first marker. He then tied a length of rope to the bottom of the pole and set out across the ice. After a short distance he repeated the process, inserting the next pole and heading off again in the same direction, to produce as straight a line of poles and rope as he could. He probably spent much of the day working his way across the smooth ice surface, covering a distance of nearly four miles. When he finished, and was happy that all the poles were in line, he returned to the start, and picked up the iron chain (possibly on the next day). In this endeavour we can safely surmise that he was following the procedures of Maupertius, whose methods and findings had been reported throughout Europe a few years earlier.

There is no record of what the chain looked like, but almost certainly it consisted of a number of carefully connected links, each perhaps a foot in length, and either 10 or 22 links in total. By laying the chain alongside the rope and stretching it taut, Murdoch was able to measure a very long straight line (a *baseline*) with considerable accuracy. When he finished he had covered a total distance of $3^3/_4$ miles. From the two ends of his line he could see the tops of nearby hills, mountains and islands. He then used a device invented about 20 years earlier, known as a theodolite, which he had been loaned by the Royal Navy. This consisted of a telescope mounted above a carefully graduated circle. With this he was able to measure a whole series of angles to these various notable points from each end of his baseline. And to be certain of their position, he constructed piles of stones and occasionally lit fires on the hilltops, to ensure his results were as accurate as he could make them. From each of these measured points, he could make sightings to additional points, along the coastline or on other islands, extending his original baseline on the ice using simple triangles and ratios to determine how far apart each point was to a considerable degree of accuracy.

MacKenzie's objective was not to make a precise land survey, although that was a partial result of his work. And his use of measured baselines and triangles was not new. But what was original was his interest in charting the coastline — recording and mapping the detailed shape of the inlets, bays, off-shore rocks, the depths off-shore, the tides and the currents. For, as he wrote in his original promotional map (one of the earliest published marketing campaigns):

> *"On this small Island alone [North Ronaldsay] about twenty British and Dutch vessels have been lost within the last 30 or 40 years many of them with very Valuable Cargoes, besides a much greater number on other Parts of that Coast; most of which might have been prevented by such a Chart of these Islands as is here proposed."*

Figure 3.1 The Island of North Ronaldsay, Orkney (© Orkney Archive)

This text is engraved in the upper right corner of the map shown in Figure 3.1. Mackenzie is the person most responsible for the development of accurate maps of coastlines, essential for the safety of vessels and the defence of island realms.

Mackenzie's work laid the foundations for the subject known as hydrography. Shortly after his retirement, when he moved to live with his nephew, also a hydrographer, in the South-West of England, the British government of the day established the UK Hydrographic Office (UKHO) to collate and map the world's coastlines for the benefit of the Navy and commercial shipping. The UK Hydrographic Office is still located close to Mackenzie's final resting place in Somerset. These days it produces detailed coastal charts for the whole world and much sub-sea data, some of which remains unpublished for security reasons. Amongst its most recent work has been the

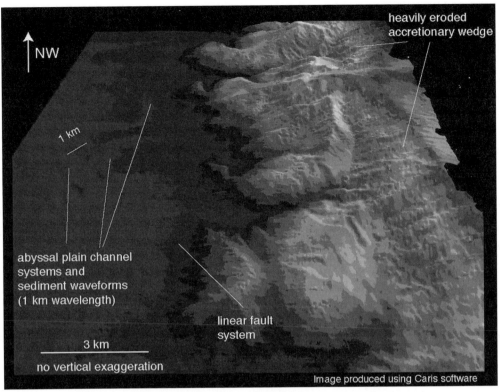

Figure 3.2 Sonar map of the seabed off the coast of Indonesia
(© Crown Copyright, UK Hydrographic Office)

mapping of sub-sea regions off the coast of Indonesia using SONAR (SOund wave Navigation Ranging) in order to assist in the development of a tsunami early warning system for the Indian Ocean region (Figure 3.2). This work follows on from the magnitude 9.3 earthquake off the west coast of northern Sumatra on December 26th 2004 at 00:58:53 UTC (Universal Coordinated Time – for more details on universal date and time measurement see Section 4.2).

Mackenzie's work relied on accurate measurement to ensure its quality, and thereby usefulness to navigators. It was 'fit for purpose' as we would now say, and it was far better than any previous work of its kind. But we also know that his worked contained many mistakes, some of which were due to the limitations of his equipment and methods, but many more were due to factors that may apply equally today. For example, lack of time, not enough funds, late payment, inadequate understanding of measurement errors and how to control or adjust them, transcription errors and publishing mistakes.

Measurement lies at the heart of our need for numbers. Whether we are measuring distances, heights, angles, volumes, weights, time, voters or the ingredients for a cake, we need to record, understand and process values in a consistent, *standardised* manner. This idea, the notion of standardised weights and measures, is a relatively recent one. In Murdoch Mackenzie's time most maps of Scotland were shown with a scale in "Scottish Miles" (bigger than English Miles) and did not show longitude (East-West position) at all — Mackenzie's Orkney maps show the zero degree meridian passing through the small town of Kirkwall, on the largest island in the group — the idea of a global meridian based on Greenwich had yet to be realised.

This problem of measurement standards, which affected the whole world at the time, remains with us to the present day. For example, on 23rd September 1999 the NASA Mars Orbiter vehicle was lost, at a mission cost of $125m, because as CNN reported at the time:

> "a Lockheed Martin engineering team used English [Imperial] units of measurement while the agency's team [NASA] used the more conventional metric system for a key spacecraft operation..."

3.2   The Danish great foot

I am not sure whether Danish people have especially large feet, but the Danish notion of a foot length in Murdoch Mackenzie's day was different and larger than a foot in most other countries — in fact it was roughly $1/_2$ inch longer than in England.

Prior to the standardisation of distance measurements (yard and metre) measurements were based on human characteristics: the digit, the hand (still used for the height of horses and now specified as 4 inches), the span, the foot, the cubit (elbow to fingertips) and the pace. Because such measures varied substantially, even within individual countries, throughout history attempts at standardisation were made. The usual procedure was to declare that a particular strip of wood (e.g. yardstick), or inscribed lines on a particular stone or metal bar, or a particular barrel defined the official measure of the government of the time and place concerned. Every country, and often every region or even town, used its own systems and standards of measurement. In France it has been estimated that as many as 250,000 different measurement standards existed in the mid 18th century. The situation had become seriously out of control!

Resolving this problem took a very long time, using the Earth itself as the central unit of measure. This involved making detailed measurements and then calculating the length of an arc on the surface of the Earth from the Equator to Pole very precisely and agreeing to define this total length as 10,000,000 units or "metres". This unit of measure was then cast into platinum-iridium bars and kept in a vault in Paris as the world standard — the foundations of metric measurement was laid, if only everyone would agree to its use!

Today we no longer use metal bars as the length standard, as we know that their size changes with atmospheric conditions, physical stress and time. Instead we rely on measurement of the speed of light to define our length standard, using the relationship: *speed=distance x time*. So a speed of 60 miles an hour means that given an interval of time, e.g. 1 minute, we can compute the distance covered, in this example 1 mile, as there are 60 minutes in an hour. The speed of light (in a vacuum) is a universal constant, known to a very high degree of accuracy, so we can take this as a first fixed value, L, and then consider how far light would travel in one second. How to carry out this measurement is not at all obvious, but is explained is some detail in the next sub-Section.

L is like Mackenzie's baseline on the frozen lake, but in this case it is about 176,000 miles or 300,000 (3×10^5) kilometres in length. So we divide this new baseline, L, by roughly 300 million (3×10^8) to obtain a fixed interval, which we then *define* as a metre (1/1000th of a kilometre or 10^{-3} kilometres). There is obviously a chicken-and-egg problem here, in that the constant L was

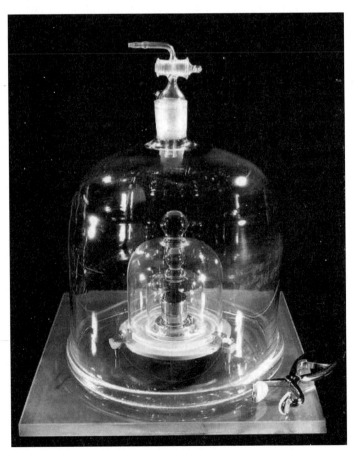

Figure 3.3 The International Standard Kilogram
(© Bureau International des Poids et Mesures (BIPM))

Description	Definition
"Imperial measures" Foot/Yard/Chain/ Furlong/Mile/League	**Foot:** an English foot was (and is) 12 inches. In the late 18th century there were other measurements for the 'foot', varying from 11.172 English inches for the Amsterdam Foot, to 12.465 English inches for the Danish Great Foot. 3 to the yard in all cases.
	Pace (passus): 5 feet (actually a Roman double pace of 30 inches/step)
	Ell: widely used throughout Europe, a Scots Ell was 37 inches, an English Ell was 45 inches (often used for fabric)
	Yard: Originally the yard was based on the word girth or girdle, a waist measurement. An initial standard yard was defined in Elizabethan times (1588), based on the earlier yard or 'ulna' of Edward I
	Fathom: 6 feet or 2 yards (roughly the same as a French *toise*)
	Chain: 22 yards, made from 100 links (for surveying). Note: 10 chains x 1 chain=1 acre; a Scots chain=24 ell or 74 feet, thus a Scots acre was larger than an English acre
	Furlong: 220 yards (a furrow long) – probably related to the Roman measurement, the Stadion
	Mile (English/British): 5280 feet (8 furlongs) – defined in 1595
	A mile had previously been taken as the Roman mile (literally 1000 'mille passus' or double paces, c.1618 yards/5000 feet); 69½miles ≈ one degree in Britain
	Mile (Scottish): Defined in Scottish Statute as 1184 paces or 5920 feet.
	Mile (Geometrical/Italian): 2038.6 yards, or one minute of arc of longitude taken at the equator (60 geometrical miles=one degree)
	League (English): 3 Geometrical miles
	1742: Yard standardised in England by the Royal Society. In 1737 Graham and Sisson made and divided two standard yards for London and Paris, one of which became the Royal Society's main reference measure
	1832: there was no legal length standard in the U.S. until this date when a bronze yard was purchased from England to act as the standard
	1844: New yard standard bar cast in bronze and defined as the Imperial Standard in 1878. By 1958 this bar had shrunk by 0.0000055metres
	1856: Imperial standards finalised
Metric measures Metre/Meter	**1791:** 1/10,000,000[th] of the quarter circumference of the Earth, measured from equator to pole, through Dunkirk (French)
	1798: on completion of surveying (from Dunkirk to Mont-Jouy near Barcelona in Spain, roughly 10° due South), a standard metre in the form of three platinum bars and several iron bars were prepared and defined the world standard 'Mètre des Archives'. On 22 June 1799 the first platinum standards for both the metre and the kilogram were deposited in Paris
	1863: International Metric Convention
	1960: redefined as "the length equal to 1,650,763.73 wavelengths in a vacuum of the radiation ... of krypton-86."
	1983: redefined as "the length of the path travelled by light in a vacuum during a time interval of 1/299,792,458 of a second".
	One metre is equal to 3.28083333 US Survey feet
Nautical mile	1 minute of arc of a great circle, or 6080 feet (British Admiralty mile, equals 1.1515... times an English Mile or 1852 metres). Latitude values are not constant due to ellipsoidal shape of Earth (varies by approx 18.7m between equator and pole). This is sometimes referred to as a *Geographic Nautical Mile*. The *International Nautical Mile* was defined as being exactly 1852 metres (6076.115 feet) in 1929. The *International Air Mile* is now taken to be the same as an International Nautical Mile

Figure 3.4 Standardisation of distance measures

described in kilometres, which means 1000s of metres, but we have not yet defined a metre. The reason for this is that L was defined in terms of the previously agreed length of a metre, and this is just refinement of earlier definitions which is easier for scientists to reproduce with great accuracy under laboratory conditions anywhere in the world.

We do still use a physical 'prototype' made of platinum-iridium to define the kilogram, and it is kept under lock and key in a controlled environment by the International Bureau of Weights and Measures in Sèvres, France (see picture, Figure 3.3). The kilogram was originally defined as the mass of 1000 cubic centimetres (1 litre) of water at 4°C (thus is based on the linear measure, centimetres, 10cmx10cmx10cm), but this is not very helpful in practice (n.b. the rather subtle difference between *weight* and *mass* is explained in more detail a little later in this book — please see the discussion on gravity in Section 3.5).

The continued use of prototype (metal) kilograms is felt to be unsatisfactory by many scientists, especially those working in atomic chemistry and particle physics, where very small differences matter a great deal. At present there is no agreed solution to this problem, although some progress is being made on possible alternatives.

The table (Figure 3.4) provides a summary of the history of length measurement — as noted above, many other fields of measurement are closely linked to these timelines.

3.3 Angles, waves and music

The accurate measurement of angles is fundamental for astronomical and terrestrial observations. Angular measurement presents particular problems, since it relies on very accurate division of a circle into equal parts. A slight error in an angular measurement over a great distance could result in a very large error in estimating a related distance. For example, locating a point C correctly using a measured line (baseline) AB and angular measurements at A and B towards a hilltop at C (Figure 3.5).

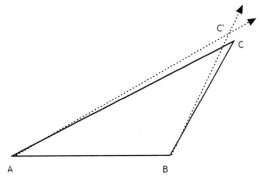

Figure 3.5 Incorrectly locating C through small errors in angular measurement

Historically angles have been measured using degrees, minutes and seconds, with 360 degrees in a circle being used for ease of division, and 60 arc minutes and 60 arc seconds providing finer subdivisions. This is believed to be based on the Babylonian number system (base60) and their use of 360 days for a year (12 months of 30 days). But this means that a 1 arc second division equals $1/(360*60*60)$ part of a circle, i.e. less than a millionth part, well beyond the possibilities of mechanical construction. On the other hand, an error of 1 arc minute over a 10km distance equates to an error of about 3 metres, so construction of equipment capable of reliably measuring angles to a fraction of an arc minute became of great importance. The theodolite used by Mackenzie is believed to have been graduated for measuring angles to 0.1 arc minutes (6 arc seconds) although achieving this level of accuracy seems highly unlikely.

Since a circle with radius $r=1$ unit has a circumference of length $C=2\pi$ units, an alternative and often more convenient angular measure is $360/C$ or $180/\pi$. This is called a *radian*, and equals roughly $57.3°$. So 2π radians$=360°$ and for any circle, radius r, an angle of θ radians times r, i.e. $r\theta=$the length of the circumference of the section of the circle included by θ.

Radians are the unit of angular measurement preferred by mathematicians and software engineers. Software tools, such as Excel, provide functions that involve angular measurement in units of radians, not degrees. Excel does provide simple conversion functions, Degrees() and Radians() for converting between the two, if you do not want to apply the conversion factor yourself.

Whilst radians are convenient, they still use the division of a circle into 360 parts as their basis. Another alternative, favoured by surveyors, is *gradians*, sometimes denoted *grad* or *gon*. Grads are based on a circle with 400 divisions, so that a quarter circle is 100 grads. They are rarely used nowadays, although they do still appear on some calculators.

The study of angles and angular measurement focuses on triangles, and the ratio of the sides of triangles, especially those with one angle being 90° (a right angle). The word *trigonometry* comes from the Latin (and Greek): *tri* (τρι) — three; *gonos* (γωνος) — cornered or angled; and *metron* (μετρον) — a measure. If we draw a simple right-angled triangle, within a circle of radius c, we can see the key ratios involved (Figure 3.6). The solid triangle shown has sides of length a, b and c, where $a^2+b^2=c^2$. The key ratios of interest are a/c and b/c since these effectively determine the angle θ (the third basic ratio, b/a, is simply $b/c \div a/c$). In our diagram θ is less than 90 degrees ($\pi/2$ radians) and is called an acute (or sharp) angle, whilst ϕ is an obtuse (blunt) angle. Since a and b can take both positive and negative values, the ratios can be positive or negative. Likewise, the angle θ can be created as the line 0X is rotated either anticlockwise or clockwise, which we regard as being in a positive or negative direction respectively.

We can use the relationship $a^2+b^2=c^2$ to obtain $b=\pm\sqrt{(c^2-a^2)}$, and hence calculate the ratio b/c for fixed values of a, keeping c constant (e.g. $c=1$). This can be viewed as looking at the ratio b/c as the line 0X is rotated in the positive (anticlockwise) direction, sweeping out an angle from $\theta=0°$ to

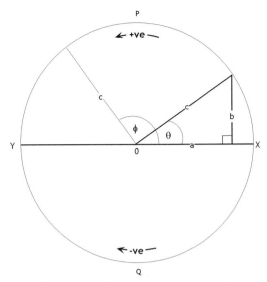

Figure 3.6 Simple angles and ratios

θ=180° from X via P to Y and then on to θ=180° as the line continues from Y via Q back to X. Over this range *a* varies from +1 to -1. Likewise, using $a=\pm\sqrt{(c^2-b^2)}$ we can calculate *a/c* for various values of *b*, which will vary from 0 to 1 and back to 0 as 0X is rotated through to 180 and then from 0 to -1 and back to 0 as 0Y is rotated via Q to X again. An extract of this kind of calculation is shown in Table 3-1.

If we plot these two ratios we find the pattern shown in Figure 3.7. The two ratios range in values

Table 3-1 Ratios and angles

a	b	c	b/c	a	b	c	a/c
1	0	1	0	1	0	1	1
0.75	0.661438	1	0.661438	0.968246	0.25	1	0.968246
0.5	0.866025	1	0.866025	0.866025	0.5	1	0.866025
0.25	0.968246	1	0.968246	0.661438	0.75	1	0.661438
0	1	1	1	0	1	1	0
−0.25	0.968246	1	0.968246	−0.66144	0.75	1	−0.66144
−0.5	0.866025	1	0.866025	−0.86603	0.5	1	−0.86603
−0.75	0.661438	1	0.661438	−0.96825	0.25	1	−0.96825
−1	0	1	0	−1	0	1	−1
−0.75	−0.66144	1	−0.66144	−0.96825	−0.25	1	−0.96825
−0.5	−0.86603	1	−0.86603	−0.86603	−0.5	1	−0.86603
−0.25	−0.96825	1	−0.96825	−0.66144	−0.75	1	−0.66144
0	−1	1	−1	0	−1	1	0
0.25	−0.96825	1	−0.96825	0.661438	−0.75	1	0.661438
0.5	−0.86603	1	−0.86603	0.866025	−0.5	1	0.866025
0.75	−0.66144	1	−0.66144	0.968246	−0.25	1	0.968246
1	0	1	0	1	0	1	1

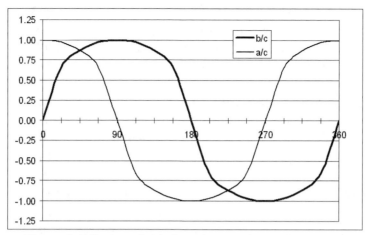

Figure 3.7 Ratios of side lengths in right angled triangles

between -1 and 1 and with a sufficient number of points will become smooth curves. The Latin for a smooth curve is *sinus* (hence the word sinuous, meaning winding curve) and from this we get the name of the mathematical function, sine or sin(), which corresponds to the ratio *b/c*. Thus sin(θ)=*b/c* and the complementary ratio, *a/c*, is known as the co-sine or cos() for short, i.e. cos(θ)=*a/c*.

Our graphs of *a/c* and *b/c* are far from ideal because we have only evaluated the ratios at a small number of points, and over the range of positive angles [0,360], or [0,2π]. It would be better to calculate and plot the two ratios for a much larger range of values of θ, from -2π to 2π say, with c=1 again. So as θ changes we map out a circle, radius c=1, with the line 0X being rotated in both positive and negative directions (see further, Box 5).

The analysis of these two simple ratios has led us from a simple, well understood examination of triangles, into quite a surprising pattern of curves and functions. What is more, many naturally occurring phenomena can be modelled using precisely these curves, either taken singly or in combination. These phenomena include: the way in which a taut string vibrates when plucked; the way sound and music is transmitted through air; the manner in which seismic events (earth-quakes, explosions) are transmitted through the Earth's crust; and the way light and radio signals are transmitted in air, water and empty space.

Speech, for example, can be measured by recording the patterns of vibrations made in the air over time, and then analysing these in terms of their *frequencies* (the number of vibrations or cycles per second, say) and their strength (loudness or *amplitude*). The human ear can hear sounds in the range 20 cycles per second (or Hertz, abbreviated as Hz), which are very low or deep sounds, to 20,000Hz (20kHz, very high pitched, almost inaudible squeaks). One cycle is like

---

Box 5. Sine and Cosine values for -2π≤x≤2π

The graph below provides a plot of the values, for both sin() and cos(), with θ or *x* in the range [-2π,2π] i.e. [-6.28..., +6.28...], where the negative range means we have rotated the angle in a clockwise direction rather than an anticlockwise direction. To do this we will use the built-in Excel functions sin() and cos():

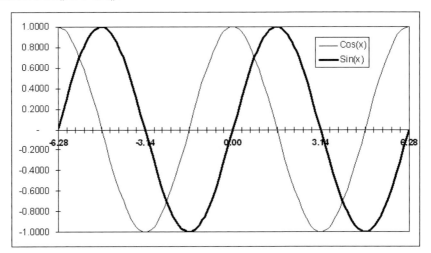

From the graph it is easy to see that the two curves have the same shape, one being shifted by π/2 (3.14.../2) from the other, so we can deduce several simple relationships. For example: look at the point at the centre of the horizontal axis, *x*=0. At this point sin(0)=0, but we can also see that sin(0+π/2)=sin(π/2)=+1. This is the same as cos(0), i.e. +1. More generally, following the pattern of the two curves, we can see that sin(*x*+π/2)=cos(*x*). Now look at cos(*x*+π/2) where *x*>0. As *x* increases to +π/2 the cosine curve goes down towards -1. At the same time sin(*x*) is increasing towards 1 in exactly the same pattern, hence cos(*x*+π/2)=-sin(*x*). We can also see from the graph that sin(*x*)=sin(*x*+2π), and cos(*x*)=cos(*x*+2π). Finally, because we know that $a^2+b^2=c^2$ we have $a^2/c^2+b^2/c^2=1$ hence $\sin^2(x)+\cos^2(x)=1$. Computation of sin(*x*) and cos(*x*) for any angle *x* is treated in Part II.

one complete set of sin() values from 0, to +1, to 0 to -1 and back to 0. The range for speech, and incidentally the top note on a piano, extends up to about 4000Hz (4kHz). Using this knowledge many familiar items of audio technology have been developed, such as FM and AM radio (Frequency and Amplitude based transmission), telephones, loud speakers and stereo systems.

To illustrate some of these ideas, suppose we add two or three distinct sounds together, as if we played a chord of three notes A, C and E on the middle section of a piano. Each note would have a distinct frequency, say A=220Hz, C=261Hz and E=329Hz, as can be seen on the piano layout (Figure 3.8). Note that the values for each 'A' key are double the previous one, so A1=55Hz and A2=110Hz — this defines an octave, the 8 note division of the normal scale used in most music.

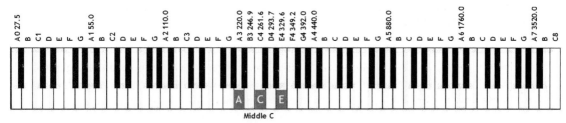

Figure 3.8 Piano keyboard and modern tuning frequencies

We can illustrate the kind of sound wave pattern created by pressing these three keys simultaneously on an idealised perfect piano, by setting $W=\sin(At)+\sin(Ct)+\sin(Et)$, where t is time and using the following nominal values for A, C and E: A=2.20, C=2.61, E=3.29. Figure 3.9 shows the result of this process. As can be seen, the wave form for A goes up and down a little slower than that for C and E, and when all three are combined by adding them together the result is a more complex waveform representing the combined sound generated.

What is remarkable about this process is that often we can reverse it (this was discovered by the French mathematician Joseph Fourier in 1807). We can record a complicated pattern of some continuously varying wave-like data such as speech over time or light from a star, and break it down into its component parts in terms of sin() and cos() functions. For example, when different chemicals are heated to high temperatures they start to glow — omitting energy in the form of light. The frequencies of the light (seen as different colours in the visible part of the spectrum) are different for different chemicals. If we receive light from some unknown source, say a distant

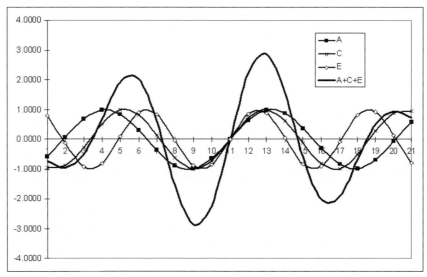

Figure 3.9 Composite wave form for the chord ACE

star, we can analyse its frequency pattern to help identify the mix of chemicals that make up that star. Similar techniques are used to analyse speech patterns, economic time series data, the surface and interior structure of the Earth, and the chemical constituents of mineral samples.

Visible light has a very high frequency and very short wavelength when compared with sound: for example green light has a frequency of around 6×10^{14}Hz and a wavelength of around 500 nanometres (a nanometre is one billionth of a metre, or $1/10^9$ metres). Radio waves, by contrast, have much lower frequency/longer wavelength patterns — Medium Wave radio operates in the range 30kHz-300kHz whilst VHF (Very High Frequency) is in the range 30MHz-300MHz, the latter with a wavelength of between 1 metre and 100mm, which is one reason why the radio is affected by its position in a room or as you move around close to its aerial.

I noted earlier that the human ear can distinguish sounds up to around 4000Hz. This frequency means that the air is vibrating 4000 times a second, and this results in our eardrum vibrating at the same frequency, transmitting this through the tiny bones in our middle ear, to nerve fibres in our inner ear that identify the frequency and pass this information to our brain to interpret. In addition the sound may be loud or soft, i.e. have different amplitudes. Suppose we have an electronic (digital) device capable of measuring the frequency of sound at very small distinct time intervals. It turns out that in order to do this in a way that allows you to reconstruct the original wave, you need to sample at twice the value of the highest frequency you are interested in, having taken care to remove (filter out) any higher frequencies first. So for human speech our device needs to sample 8000 times a second to detect and record 4000Hz.

But speech has varying loudness or amplitude as well. Let us imagine that for amplitude we only need to distinguish a limited number of levels, e.g. 256, or 2^8 levels, from very quiet to very loud. Now we have a total of 8000x8 positions to sample, and if each is coded as a 1 or 0, this is 64,000 bits, or 64kbits for a single voice channel. This is the figure that is used in all modern telecommunications as the basis of most voice and data transmission. When blocked up into collections of 32 channels, it gives the 2Mbit combined speed that is the next step up in the transmission hierarchy, familiar to those using high speed leased lines, cable and DSL networks from their homes and offices (in the USA 24 channels are used to form a composite trunk connection rather than 32, giving T1 or 1.5Mbit services).

Of course, a long string of 1's and 0's recording 64,000 values for each second will almost always contain long sections or *runs* which are all 0's or all 1's. Instead of keeping a sequence of 28 0's, for example, we could code this *run* as (28,0), which would be shorter or compressed. Many forms of information, when reduced to strings of 1's and 0's (i.e. digital form) including sounds and pictures, can be compressed using techniques such as this. Not all such techniques will preserve the characteristics of the original data perfectly (and are described as lossy, since they accept some loss of quality). But often we can retain acceptable quality speech using perhaps 8kbits/second or less after compression, allowing far more information to be transmitted over a link of given capacity.

Hi fidelity (HiFi) music is more demanding, so we tend to sample at higher frequencies (more times each second) and tolerate less compression than we might accept for speech. For audio CDs the standard sampling rate is 44.1kHz with 16 bits for amplitude rather than the 8bits we used for speech. The use of 44.1kHz sampling comes from enabling sounds up to 22.05kHz (the very high-pitched squeaks we mentioned earlier) to be recorded digitally (2x22.05=44.1). The net result is that each second of CD-quality sound requires 44,100x16=705,600 bits to be stored, or twice this figure to provide stereo. Assuming no data compression is applied, 74 minutes of sound tracks would require around 780 million bytes of storage capacity (747Mbytes, where 1Mbyte=2^{20}bytes=1,048,576bytes). The choice of 74 minutes has a disputed origin, but is often stated as being based on the time needed for a complete recording of Beethoven's 9th Symphony on a single disc — actually Beethoven's 9th requires around 70 minutes). Audio CDs record information in blocks or sectors, each containing 2352 bytes (8bit chunks) of data, and a total of 333,000 sectors are provided on every CD, giving 333,000x2532 bytes capacity, or 747Mbytes.

Once people realised that a CD stored so much information just for audio, it was a short step to enable their use for data and images. However, for data it is essential that no information is lost, or recorded or replayed with errors, so from every 2352 byte sector, 2048 bytes is reserved for data, 256 bytes for error detection/correction bits, and 48 bits are reserved for future use. The net result is that a standard data CD only stores 747x2048/2353 Mbytes or 650 Mbytes.

3.4   Measuring the speed of light, c

We decided to test the Theory of Relativity. Jeff got a torch... and stood on this side of the room.

"Now Jeff, switch the torch on and shout 'go' and I will time how long it takes to see the light and the speed..."

"Hold on, if you say 'go' that's the speed of sound, and I would hear that after I've seen the light, so say 'go' slightly earlier... and you time how early you've... (frustrated) Oh, it's a million miles an hour! I said a million billion... no one can tell! No one can run that fast!"

"And mass... can you weigh the torch for the mass, please? Can you weigh it in a vacuum? Can you weigh it near a vacuum, then? You can weigh it near a vacuum cleaner, that's great!"

Eddie Izzard, Definite Article, 1995

Despite appearances, Eddie Izzard's comedy sketch is not totally removed from reality. As I describe below, the speed of light has been accurately measured using a beam of light shone across a room, but with "Jeff" being replaced by a mirror and not a vacuum cleaner in sight! And as we have just discovered, even ignoring its importance in Relativity Theory, we need to know the speed of light if we want to be certain of exactly how long a metre is.

The earliest reasonable estimates of the speed of light came from observations by telescope of Jupiter's largest moon, Io, in the late 17th century. The period of this moon's orbit (i.e. the time taken to go right around Jupiter) appeared to vary through the course of the Earth's year, differing by approximately 22 minutes at the extremes. These extremes were identified as being between the times when the Earth was closest to Jupiter or furthest from it, so it seemed that the difference in Earth's proximity to Jupiter and the time for light to travel to the Earth was the explanation. In 1676, based on the estimated size of the Earth's orbit around the Sun (a diameter thought to be about 283 million kilometres at the time), the Danish astronomer Ole Römer announced that the speed of light was around 214,000 km/sec (modified here to metric units). By 1809 this figure had been refined to 300,300 km/sec using the same methods and more observations. But detailed analysis of the data used showed that even this latter figure was only approximate. Better estimates were sought, under controlled conditions, but there was doubt whether such an experiment could be conducted on Earth. These concerns arose because of the short distances available on Earth and the effects of the air and possibly the unknown medium through which light was thought to travel, the *æther*.

In 1879 the speed of light in air was measured with great care by a 24 year old USA-based physicist, Albert Michelson, by shining a beam of light across a room and measuring the time for it to travel across a known distance. In his initial experiment the room was 45 ft long and 14 ft wide, and the light source used was the Sun, whose rays were focused using a lens into a narrow beam. The beam was reflected via a mirror that was rotating rapidly (powered by air pressure from a steam driven pump) through a hole in the building to a distant mirror, from which it was reflected straight back to the revolving mirror (see Figure 3.10, diagram i). Because the revolving mirror would have turned slightly in this interval, the reflected light beam was reflected again but in a slightly different direction (see Figure 3.10, diagram ii).

By measuring the size of this deflection and knowing the path length of the beam and rotational speed of the mirror, the speed of light can be calculated. Suppose the mirror is rotating at 240 revolutions per minute (rpm), and the fixed mirror is 490 metres from the rotating mirror. Incoming light will strike the rotating mirror and be reflected through a small hole or slit in the room to the fixed mirror and then it will be reflected straight back at the rotating mirror (980 metres covered in these two steps). But the rotating mirror will have moved a bit in this interval and the returning light beam will be deflected to a point near the original input beam from the Sun, but at a measurable distance, AB, from it.

If the deflected beam is 100mm from the incoming beam, and we let BR=RA=10 metres we can calculate the speed of light as follows: imagine that RA is the radius, *r*, of a circle; the circumference of the circle is $2\pi r = 2\pi 10,000$mm so our 100mm deflection amounts to a small part of this,

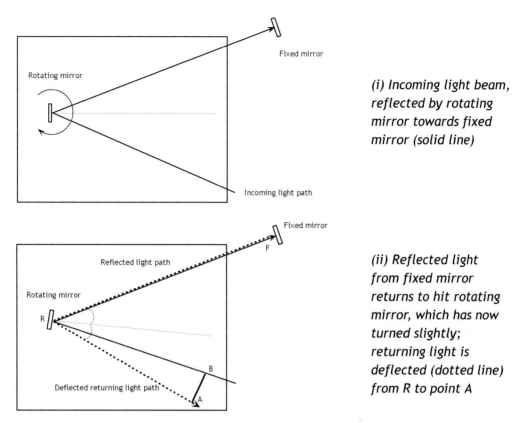

(i) *Incoming light beam, reflected by rotating mirror towards fixed mirror (solid line)*

(ii) *Reflected light from fixed mirror returns to hit rotating mirror, which has now turned slightly; returning light is deflected (dotted line) from R to point A*

Figure 3.10 Michelson's 1879 experiment

being approximately $1/2\pi100^{th}$. But this is twice the amount the mirror has turned, because reflections double the angles (see Figure 3.10, dotted lines), thus the mirror has moved by $1/4\pi100^{th}$ of one rotation. Since it rotates 240 times in one second, it rotates this very small amount in $1/(240 \times 400\pi^{th})$ part of a second. In this fleeting interval the light has travelled from B to R to F, back to R and on to A, a total of 10+980+10=1000metres, so the estimated speed of the light beam in metres covered in one second is $1000 \times 240 \times 400\pi$ m/s, or 301,593 km/sec.

In Michelson's case, for most of his observations his mirror was set to rotate at 258 rpm, the fixed mirror was just under 2000 feet (c. 605m) from the rotating mirror, the deflected path length was c. 8.7m, and he expected the average deflection would be approximately 115mm. Using his apparatus Michelson took 100 measurements over 28 days, with each reported measurement being the average of 10 repeated measurements of the displacement. Figure 3.11 shows a summary of the results of this experiment, which show an average speed of 299,875 km/sec (frequency in this diagram being the number of results recorded for each particular speed value or range).

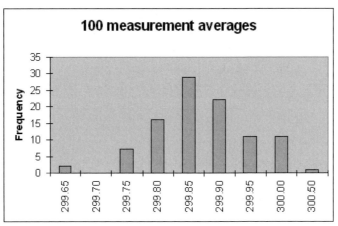

Figure 3.11 Measured average values for the speed of light

After making adjustments for temperature variations and the refractive effect of the air, Michelson announced that he estimated the speed of light *in a vacuum* was $c=299,944 \pm 51$ km/sec. This result took into account an enormous variety of factors that might influence the measurement and analysis process, but it was conducted at a fixed location.

Some scientists criticised the approach taken by Michelson because they argued that the results might have been different if the measurements had been made simultaneously but at right angles to the direction selected, or if made six months later with the Earth on the opposite side of the Sun (moving in the opposite direction as it were). Michelson sought to remedy this deficiency with a new experiment in 1881, improved further with a colleague, Edward Morley in 1887, which demonstrated that the speed of light was unaffected by these locational factors. Einstein's Special Theory of Relativity, in which the speed of light plays a pivotal role, depended on this finding, although Einstein himself said that at the time (1905) Michelson's experiments did not directly influence his work.

Many years later Michelson sought to improve on his 1879 results by taking a much longer baseline and measurements taken at altitude (with less interference from the air). His 1920s measurements were made between two mountain peaks in California using a beam of light shone from one peak onto a concave mirror on the other peak, and thence back again to an octagonal prism rotating at 32,000rpm that formed part of the timing mechanism. The baseline of some 22 miles, or separation of the apparatus on the two mountains, had been previously measured by the US Geodetic Survey over a period of two years to within 0.25 inches using tapes made of a special metal called Invar (an alloy that has almost no change with normal temperature fluctuations). Using this new arrangement Michelson estimated the speed of light to be $299,796 \pm 4$ km/sec, slightly lower than his early figure (and outside of his stated error bands). This revised figure is almost exactly the value we now use.

Increasingly accurate measurements confirmed that the speed of light appeared to be a universal constant, and relativity theory stated that this speed was unaffected by the speed or direction of motion of the observer. The speed of light was thus ideal as a basis for the *definition* of a unit of length, and in 1983 the internationally agreed unit of length (the metre) was changed to be *"...the length of the path travelled by light in vacuum during a time interval of 1/299,792,458 of a second"*.

3.5   Measuring gravity and the gravitational constant, *G*

"the variation of speed in air between balls of gold, lead, copper, porphory, and other heavy metals is so slight that in a fall of 100 cubits [about 46 metres] a ball of gold would not outstrip one of copper by as much as four fingers. Having observed this I came to the conclusion that in a medium totally void of resistance all bodies would fall with the same speed." Galileo Galilei, 1638

3.5.1 Terrestrial gravity and acceleration

If you step out of a helicopter that is hovering at 1000m, initially your speed of fall is zero metres/sec. Assuming your name is not Larry Walters and you do not have helium balloons strapped to your body, then after a very short period your speed of descent increases so that after 1 second you are falling at around 9.81m/s (about 35kms/hr or 22mph). After 2 seconds you are falling even faster, twice as fast in fact, at 19.62m/s. In theory, ignoring the effect of air resistance, you would keep *accelerating* at a constant rate of g=9.81m/s for every second, getting faster and faster until you hit the ground with a considerable bang!

Although the acceleration due to Earth's gravity, g, is a constant per unit of time, the distance you cover is not. In the first second you start falling with no speed and by the end of the second you are falling at 9.81m/s, so on average your speed in this period is 9.81/2=4.91m/s , i.e. slower in the first half a second and faster in the second half. Thus in the first second you will have fallen roughly 4.91 metres. The same occurs in the next second, since you start at 9.81m/s and finish at 19.62m/s, so your average speed is 14.72m/s in this interval. You have now fallen 4.91+14.72m=19.63m. In 10 seconds your speed has increased to 93m/s and the total distance has grown to nearly 500m (over 1500 ft) — after just over 14 seconds you will hit the ground, as can be seen from Figure 3.12. In order to calculate the distance you will fall we have added together (or integrated into one number) all the little incremental distances covered in each second.

In practice a falling human will reach a maximum velocity of around 75m/s (270 km/hr) because of air resistance, or less than this if sky diving (spread eagled). However, ignoring air resistance, you can see that the graph is not a straight line — its slope increases over time. In rough terms, after 5 seconds your total descent is about 125m (5x5x5m), after 10 seconds about 500m (5x10x10m) and after 20 seconds, about 2000m (5x20x20m) — in each case proportional to time,

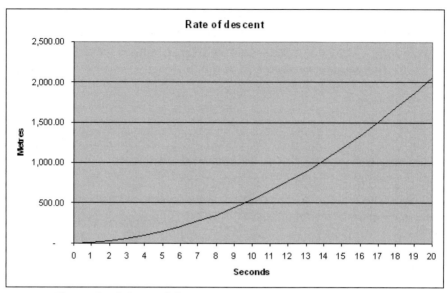

Figure 3.12 Rate of descent, free fall with no air resistance

kt^2, where k is some constant (5, i.e. $\approx g/2$). The pattern shows that the distance covered appears to be of the form $d=gt^2/2$.

If we had taken incremental steps of 0.1 seconds instead of 1 second we would have seen the same result: after 0.5 seconds 0.049m, after 1 second 4.905m, and after 2 seconds 19.620m, confirming this pattern. Letting $d=1000$metres and $g=9.81m/s^2$ we can find the exact time, in seconds, it would take to hit the ground from the formula $d=gt^2/2$. Rearranging this expression we have $t=\sqrt{(2d/g)}$ and thus $t=\sqrt{(2000/9.81)}=14.278$ seconds, consistent with our graph.

If you were pushed out of the helicopter heading downwards immediately at $b=10m/s$ instead of starting at 0m/s you would find that after 20 seconds you would have covered about 5x20x20+10x20 metres, and the formula for distance $d=gt^2+bt$ would match our results (in many texts you will find that this is written using the symbols s for distance and u for initial velocity, i.e. as $s=ut+gt^2/2$).

You can easily replicate these examples using Excel (use the built-in Convert() function if you need a quick conversion between metres and feet or kilometres and miles). It does tell us some-thing much more general about rates of change than just answering questions about gravity and descent. If any variable y has a constant positive (or negative) rate of change, a, with time t (so y is of the form $y=at+b$ where b is a constant, possibly 0) the cumulative (or integrated) effect over time is of the order $z=at^2+bt$ (where $a=g/2$ in our example); likewise, if we have data that shows a pattern such that a variable z varies as the squared power of t (or a similar variable) then it can be regarded as having an underlying constant rate of change. As an aside, those readers familiar with basic calculus will recognise these results as being the integral $z=\int y \, dt$ and its reverse operation, the differential $y=dz/dt$ (don't panic if this means nothing to you — I have provided a brief explanation of these terms in Appendix 1). In Part II I experiment with similar ideas, in this case dealing with problems involving growth and decay.

Gravitational force on the Earth, g, has a *magnitude* of approximately $g=9.81 m/s^2$ (as noted earlier the bit $/s^2$ means "per second per second", so is an acceleration and thus increases with time rather than a speed which would be just $/s$, a constant over time). It also has a *direction* which points generally to the centre of the Earth, so can be thought of as a vector. However, g varies with latitude, and is around 0.05% less at the poles than the equator — indeed, the discovery of this variation is one reason that Newton had argued that the shape of the Earth was flattened at the poles, rather like a grapefruit.

This variation affects the apparent weight of objects and influences the frequency of pendulums, so clocks with a pendulum of a given length will vary in their time-keeping depending on where they are in the world. In due course variations in the time-keeping of pendulum clocks of a fixed pendulum length became the main method by which variations in g were measured. This is possible using the simple formula derived by Dutchman Christian Huygens (1629-1695):

$t=\pi \sqrt{(l/g)}$

where t is the time taken for a pendulum to swing from one side to the other, l is the length of the pendulum and g is the magnitude of the gravitational force. Re-writing the above expression we have:

$g=\pi^2 l/t^2$

so if $l=1$ metre and $t=1$ second, we find $g=9.869 m/s^2$, or around 32 ft per second squared. In fact g is a bit less than this, because $l=1$ is not quite correct, as we shall see in a moment! Re-writing the above expression again we have:

$l=gt^2/\pi^2$

Thus, if g equals a constant, say $g=9.81 m/sec^2$ or $g=32.18$ feet/sec^2, and $t=1$, then we find $l=3.26$ feet or 0.994m, so a one second pendulum is almost exactly a metre long. From Galileo we know that, in principle, it does not matter what the pendulum is made of, although air friction, physical friction at the top of the pendulum, temperature and one or two other factors all affect the periodicity, but these factors can all be largely eliminated with very careful design.

Other factors influence both the magnitude and direction of gravity on Earth. The most important of these are distance from the centre of the Earth (gravity is greater at the bottom of a deep mine and less up in an aircraft or on top of a mountain), and variations in the density of the Earth's upper layer or crust. The latter effects are significant and can mean that a plumb line (a wire with a weight on the end) may not hang directly 'downwards' towards the centre of the Earth, but may be deflected slightly, for example influenced by the mass of very large mountains nearby. These effects were first measured in Scotland in the 1780s, but came to prominence during the measuring of the Great Arc, the detailed mapping of the Indian sub-continent from its Southern tip northwards to the Himalayas by George Everest and others.

3.5.2 Universal gravitational constant, G

The gravitational constant, G, is not the value recorded for the gravitational force, g, at the Earth's surface — the latter varies considerably across the globe and is dependent on the mass of the Earth (including local variations such as the influence of mountains), the Sun and the Moon. G is a *universal* constant, like the speed of light discussed earlier. To understand these ideas better we need to be confident of the meanings of the terms weight, mass, force and acceleration. Your *weight* on Earth is not the same as your weight if you were standing on the Moon or adrift in space, but your *mass* (the amount of matter you are made of) is unchanged. Weight is dependent on the value of gravity, which is much less on the Moon than the Earth (the strength of the gravitational force on the surface of the Moon is about 1/6th of its value at the Earth's surface). More precisely, we can say weight=mass times gravitational acceleration. But from Newton we have the *definition of force* as force=mass times acceleration ($F=ma$), so in this sense weight is equivalent to force. The terminology is confusing, and is often misused. However, we will work with it for the moment and look at the idea of a universal gravitational constant, G. G is the constant in Newton's formula which states that the attractive force, F, between two bodies is proportional to the product of their masses and inversely proportional to the square of their separation:

$F=GM_1M_2/r^2$ where M_1 and M_2 are the masses of two objects (e.g. the Earth and the Sun) r units apart

The value for G, the constant of proportionality in this equation, was first measured in 1798 by Henry Cavendish using two bags of sand suspended on a beam from a wire. He obtained the figure $G=6.75\pm0.05 \times 10^{-11}$ units (the units are Nm^2/kg^2 — see further, Box 6), an astonishing result which has hardly been bettered in over two centuries.

Although Newton believed that both light and gravity acted instantaneously, it has been known for some years that gravitational effects travel through space (sometimes described as gravitational waves). In September 2002 the speed of gravity was measured using the transit of Jupiter across the path of a distant stellar body (a quasar), rather as the speed of light had been studied during solar eclipses. This exercise confirmed, as predicted by Einstein's theories, that gravity travels at or very close to the speed of light.

Box 6. Measuring the universal gravitational constant, G

Cavendish attached two bags of sand to either end of a horizontal bar and hung the entire contraption from a thread or fibre in the middle. He then measured the twist effect upon this arrangement caused by other large objects nearby, in an arrangement known as a torsion balance. Recent estimates of the size of G have been based on arrangements of this type, although with more sophisticated equipment. The picture below shows a typical modern arrangement, reminiscent of Michelson's experiments:

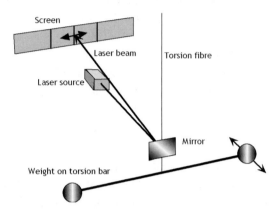

The horizontal bar is set in motion, allowing it to oscillate back and forth, turning the mirror and tracing a light beam onto the screen. The frequency of the beam trace is timed accurately, and then a large object is placed near the torsion bar and the change in frequency measured.

The currently accepted value for G is 6.672459×10^{-11} Nm^2/kg^2, where N is short for Newtons, adopted in 1960 as the internationally agreed unit of force used in recognition of Sir Isaac Newton (1 Newton is equivalent to roughly 102 grams at the Earth's surface, hence a Kilogram is about 10 Newtons – this comes from $F=ma$, so $m=F/a$, and taking $m=1$ Kilogram or 1000 grams and $a=g=9.81$ we have N=1000/9.81 grams=102 grams). The value for G is still a bit obscure, so let us take a practical example. Suppose we have two large steel bars, each weighing 10 metric tonnes (10,000kgs), which are hung from separate wires at a distance of 1 metre apart (i.e. 1 metre between their centres of gravity). Then using Newton's formula for F we have $F=G \times 10^4 kg \times 10^4 kg / 1m^2$, and if we substitute the expression for G the units $kg \times kg = kg^2$ and m^2 cancel out and we have $F \approx 7 \times 10^{-3}$ Newtons. We already know that 1 Newton is equivalent to 102 grams, so we have $F \approx 7 \times 10^{-1}$ grams, i.e. 0.7 grams. So the gravitational attraction *between* these two huge weights is only equivalent to the weight of a few grains of sand on the Earth's surface – it is thus a *very* weak force.

4 TIMES AND DATES

4.1   Definition and measurement of time

As we have just seen, the definition of the metre, and with it many other internationally agreed measures, is now essentially based on time measurement. This raises the question, how do we measure time? This is a fascinating subject extending over the entire history of civilisation, but in all cases is based, like the definition of the original metre, on the behaviour of the Earth. For time measurement, the rotation of the Earth about its axis provides our constant unit. We can call this unit, D, for Day. We then divide this supposed constant D into smaller divisions, hours (24), minutes (60) and seconds (60), for use in time measurement devices (clocks). Thus there are S=24x60x60=86,400 seconds in each day and this provides the basic unit of time measurement.

Unfortunately the rotational speed of the Earth is *not* constant — it systematically varies throughout the year as the Earth moves around the Sun — sometimes it rotates faster than the average and sometimes slower. This variation was known even to the Babylonian astronomers, because it can be observed by checking the positions of the 'fixed' stars in the night sky throughout the year. There can be as much as 30 seconds difference between the annual average and any particular day, and over a series of days this difference can grow to as much as 17 minutes. For this reason one needs to work with an average, or 'mean' day if we want constant seconds. A second of time was therefore defined very early on with reference to the mean solar day, and this was the situation until 1956. Some clocks, especially those made in the 17th and 18th centuries, included an engraved or printed table or diagram of the "equation of time", which gave the difference between the clock time and solar time, important if you wanted to use or check a clock against a sundial.

As understanding of the rotational behaviour of the Earth has improved, the definition of a unit of time, the second, has also improved. From 1956 to 1967 seconds were defined with reference to an entire year rather than a single day. A year is roughly 365.25 days, which is S=31,557,600 seconds. Using observations of the stars relative to the Earth and Sun, it is possible to determine the precise length of a terrestrial year, and this resulted in the agreed value for S being 31,556,925.9747 seconds, or 365.2422 days. With 365 days in a normal year we need to adjust the calendar every 4 years by 1 day to correct for the missing 0.25s — this is why we have leap years. But the new definition of a second shows that this slightly overestimates the length of a year. This can be corrected by an additional leap year rule, which states that you do not add a day for years divisible by 100 (i.e. centuries) that do not leave a remainder of 200 or 600 when divided by 900. This rather complicated rule means that the year 1900 was a leap year but 2000 was not. The result is called the Revised Julian Calendar (Julian being named after Julius Caesar), and gives a year length of 365.24222...days, which is excellent for all practical purposes. This Calendar was introduced in 1923 as a minor modification to the previous version of the Julian Calendar (also known as the Gregorian Calendar), which dates from 1582.

The standardised International Calendar does not correspond to the Religious calendars used in many parts of the world. For example, the Muslim calendar is based on the lunar cycle, and uses 12 months of either 29 or 30 days (alternating) to give a year of 354 days (355 in a leap year). The Jewish calendar is more complicated, requiring leap months in some years. Such calendars 'slide' with respect to the International Calendar, but can be reconciled with it when necessary.

The motion of the Earth is not entirely constant over long periods of time. It 'wobbles' on its axis rather than just spinning, its rotation is affected by ice ages which have altered the Earth's shape slightly over time, and it is gradually slowing down due to the effect of the pull of the Moon on the sea and mass of the Earth — this latter effect is known to be large over geological timescales, but for most purposes can be ignored. To eliminate some of these physical issues, from 1967 onwards the definition of a second has been altered once more, and is now based on the precise measurement of time as derived from the radioactive behaviour of Caesium 133. Thus our measures for lengths, volumes, weights etc., and time are based ultimately on the behaviour of Caesium.

4.2   Digital representation of time

What about times and dates used in computers and digital equipment? There are many reasons why date and time information may be stored in a computer, but these fall into two main categories:

(i)   as information, indicating for example when a letter was written or a data item was input or updated; and

(ii) for processing, for example calculating the elapsed time between a set of events or computing how long a certain operation may take.

In the first category it is important to ensure that the information stored is unambiguous, and for example will not result in confusion when *output* in North American form (YY-DD-MM) rather than European/International format (YY-MM-DD), as we saw earlier. This means that dates need to be stored using numbers, and then be converted on output to the desired format. In the second category it is essential that times and dates are stored in a convenient form for processing, perhaps as the number of seconds elapsed since some date in the distant past. Hence both categories of usage require that dates and times be stored as numbers.

But there are a lot of seconds in a day, let alone a century (over 3000 million), so deciding on a start day could be quite important. When computers first provided these facilities they relied on simple rules for generating dates and times. Because such capabilities only became widely available in the 1970s, and computers had limited data storage at the time, forward dates and times were recorded relative to a specific start value, often 1st January 1970 (1970-01-01). Dates and times were then stored relative to this start date, typically using two digits for the years, so 70-99 meant 1970-1999. Some 16-bit computers (with a maximum signed stored number of 32767) stored days as (Year-1970)x1000+DayOfYear, which then expired (became unusable) at the start of 2003.

A similar problem, which could have been extremely serious, occurred on the 21st August 1999, just before midnight. This related to the dates and times used by the Global Positioning Satellite (GPS) network, essential to navigators at sea and in the air throughout the world. GPS depends on extremely accurate atomic clocks that are installed in each GPS satellite. The original GPS system stored and transmitted the date part of their time signal relative to a start date of 6th January 1980, known as the "GPS Epoch", using a 10-bit field for week numbers (GPS time within each week is provided in seconds, from 0 to 604,800 restarting every Sunday morning at 00:00hrs). The use of 10 bit week numbers meant that after 1023 weeks (i.e. 2^{10}-1 weeks) — in August 1999 — the clocks would effectively be set back to week 0 (i.e. in 1980). Few people outside of the industry were aware of this issue, and many of those who were aware chose not to take a flight that day! It was left to the manufacturers of receiver equipment to amend the software or hardware in the receivers so that the devices continued to work after 22nd August 1999. Some devices continued to work but just showed the date as being wrong, whilst others gave wrong readings or failed altogether.

Many systems store dates in seconds from a given start date (or cycle on a weekly basis, as with GPS time). For some of these systems two digit years (e.g. 70-99) were extended as the year 2000 approached to permit the values 00-38, thus enabling two-digit dates to be extended through to 2038. The reason for the extension to 2038 rather than 2069 is that within a 32-bit hardware architecture, with dates and times stored in seconds from 1970-01-01, there are 2^{31} seconds available, so values will run until 19th January 2038, after which systems will fail unless modified in good time (a new Millennium bug problem, but well into the future).

As we have seen from the discussion on computers, dates and times, agreeing how a second is defined is only part of the problem. To be able to say what the date and time are at any particular instant we need to have a globally agreed start time and then calculate forwards from this time. This time is known as Coordinated Universal Time, or UTC, and it started on January 1st 1972. UTC is maintained using atomic clocks, and adjusted occasionally by the insertion of 'leap seconds' to correct for the fact that the Earth is slowing down by about 1 second every 18 months (so every now and then there are officially 61 seconds in a minute). There were 22 adjustments between 1972 and 2000, 13 occurring since the GPS satellites were launched in 1980 — and since the latter use atomic clocks that are not adjusted, they show a time that deviated from UTC by 13 seconds by the end of 1999. Only one leap second has been added since that date (at the end of 2005) so 14 seconds was the disparity at the start of 2006.

These kinds of issue explain why there has been so much concern with the way in which computers store date and time information. There are many pitfalls in this field, and many so-called critical dates and times in the years to come. The enormous problems surrounding the Year 2000 has made most people aware of such issues, but there are sure to be some that appear unexpectedly out of the woodwork in the years to come.

Assuming that the date and time information is correct, the format for display is a secondary issue, but one which warrants consideration. The International Standards Organisation (ISO) standard for date storage is the ISO 8601 specification. In terms of ISO 8601, dates should be stored in the format YYYY-MM-DD, requiring 8 decimal digits, with 4 digits for the year. This is also represented by CCYY-MM-DD, where CC is the century portion of the 4-digit year. Times are normally stored in Integer seconds, but decimal parts of seconds may also be provided and used. Simple "random" number generators provided as software functions in many computer programs often use the number of seconds since midnight as a 'seed' or starting value, since this changes continuously during the day (see further, Section 12.5).

5   NUMBER GROUPS

In the subsections that follow I describe the main number groups that you are likely to encounter. Some of these are distinct groups or sets, whilst others are selections from within these sets. For example, prime numbers are a subset of the Integers. In mathematical texts the main groups are often referred to by letters in outline as shown below:

Name	Naturals (positive Integers)	Integers	Rationals (fractions)	Reals	Complex (imaginaries)
	$\mathbb{N}$	$\mathbb{Z}$	$\mathbb{Q}$	$\mathbb{R}$	$\mathbb{C}$
Examples	1, 2, 3...	...-3, -2, -1, 0, 1, 2, 3...	12/97, 1/500	12.98, 5, -203.00, π	3+4i or (3,4)

5.1   Integers and Integer sequences

"God created the integers: all else is the work of man", Leonard Kronecker (1823-1891)

The set of all whole numbers, including zero and the negative whole numbers, is called the Integers. The letter **Z** is often used to denote the set of all Integers, sometimes shown in bold or partial outline to avoid confusion. If negative numbers and zero are excluded the term Natural numbers, **N**, is often used, although positive Integers is a more helpful name (often denoted by Z^+). The term Integer derives directly from the Latin (integer) meaning untouched, intact or entire. This notion was extended to use within mathematics in the 16th century as: "a number or quantity denoting one or more whole things or units; a whole number or undivided quantity".

Integers are the building blocks of counting, and turn out to be much more complicated than appears at first sight. The positive Integers can be separated into three distinct groups, based on how they may be divided by other Integers leaving no remainder:

- {1}: the number 1 — is the only number with only one divisor, itself
- {p}: the set of numbers that have two divisors, these being 1 and *p*
- {n}: the set of all other positive Integers, having more than two divisors

5.1.1 Prime numbers
"Prime numbers are what is left when you have taken all the patterns away. I think prime numbers are like life. They are very logical but you could never work out the

rules, even if you spent all your time thinking about them." The teenager Christopher Boone in Chapter 19 (i.e. 8, because he counts in prime numbers not Integers) of "The curious incident of the dog in the night-time", by Mark Haddon, 2003

The set {p} is known as the *Prime Numbers*, the first few being {2,3,5,7,11,13,17,19,23,29...}. The set {n} starts {4,6,8,9,10,12,14,...}. Every number in the set {n} can be written as the product of numbers from the set {p} in a *unique* manner (or *factorisation*). Thus 4=2*2 (i.e. 2^2), 8=2*2*2 (i.e. 2^3), 12=2^2*3, and 10725=3*5^2*11*13. This surprising result is not at all obvious, but has been rigorously proved. It is called the Fundamental Theorem of Arithmetic.

There has always been considerable interest in the set {p}, starting with the famous proof by the Greek mathematician, Euclid, that there are an infinite number of primes (see further, Section 5.7 on Infinity and Infinite sets). Particular attention has been paid to prime numbers in recent years. This is partly because they turn out to be very useful for encrypting data. I cover this topic in Part II, where we shall use large prime numbers to encrypt a credit card number so that the information can be securely transferred electronically. The process relies on the fact that given two very large prime numbers, p and q (the keys to the encryption process), the product $n=p*q$ is an extremely large number. This product is only divisible in one way (as I have indicated earlier) and finding this particular factorisation of n is extremely difficult. If it is so difficult that it would take the best computers in the world many decades to calculate, it is regarded as being a strong or secure encryption method. When you read that an e-commerce site is using 64- or 128-bit encryption, it is referring to the size of prime number (expressed in binary) used in this process. In the case of 128-bit key, this is a 39 digit number, i.e. very large indeed. Much larger prime numbers are known to exist.

Many of the largest primes discovered to date have the form 2^p-1 and are known as *Mersenne Primes*, M_p, after the French mathematician Marin Mersenne (Box 7). We know that M_7 or $2^7-1=127$ is prime, and that $2^{127}-1$ is also a prime number, with 39 digits. However, $2^{257}-1$, which has 78 digits, is not prime. This result was proven in 1931 but only recently have its three factors been determined, the smallest of which is a 15 digit number. Mersenne primes are very scarce — in late 2003 a researcher, Josh Findley, discovered the 41st known Mersenne prime, $2^{24036583}-1$, a number having 7,235,733 decimal digits. This number has recently been superseded (February 18, 2005) by eye-specialist Dr. Martin Nowak from Germany, who has found the new largest known prime, $2^{25964951}-1$, a number with 7,816,230 digits. A prize of $100,000 has been offered for the first person to identify a Mersenne prime with more than 10 million digits.

5.1.2 Perfect numbers

Some Integers can be written as the sum of the Integers they can be divided by, including 1 but excluding themselves: for example 6=1+2+3 and 28=1+2+4+7+14. Such Integers are called *Perfect Numbers*, and to date the only Perfect Numbers that have been identified are even and end in either 6 or 28. It is not known if there are any odd Perfect numbers, but if there are it has been

Box 7. Marin Mersenne (1588-1648)

Marin Mersenne attended school at the College of Mans in France and then, from 1604, spent five years in the Jesuit College at La Flèche in Anjou, at the same time as Descartes (Box 4). From 1609 to 1611 he studied theology at the Sorbonne. Mersenne joined the religious order of the Minims in 1611. Mersenne continued his education within the order at Nigeon and then at Meaux.

He returned to Paris in 1612. Mersenne corresponded with other eminent mathematicians, including Galileo, and he played a major role in communicating mathematical knowledge throughout Europe at a time when there were no scientific journals. He is best known as the friend and advisor of Descartes, and for his investigations into prime numbers.

shown that they must be extremely large. Even Perfect numbers are directly related to the Mersenne primes I have just described: if M_p is a Mersenne prime, then $2^{p-1}M_p$ is a Perfect Number. So $M_3=7$ and $28=2^2\times7$, $M_5=31$ and $496=2^4\times31$.

5.1.3 Modular arithmetic

In traditional arithmetic, the set of possible Integers stretches from positive infinity to negative infinity. When an operation such as addition or multiplication is carried out a new number is formed within this infinite set. Modular arithmetic, by contrast, works with a restricted set of values, such as 0,1,2,3,4,5,6 and operations on these numbers cause the results to 'wrap around' when they reach the largest value, or *modulus*. This is sometimes known as clock arithmetic, owing to its similarity to the hour hand on a clock, progressing through 1 o'clock, 2 o'clock etc. until it returns to the top of the dial where it starts again at 12 o'clock. With modular arithmetic the set of values are normally positive and/or negative Integers, and typically these include 0. So for modulo 12 arithmetic (*mod* 12) the allowable digits are the set {0,1,2,3...,11} rather like a clock, but with 0 used in place of 12. Addition and multiplication operations are carried out in the usual way, but the result is then divided by the modulus, in our example 12, and the remainder is the value retained. So 8+5=13/12=1. Actually we should not write = in this case since it is more of an equivalence or congruence than an equality. The symbol for equivalence is ≡ so we would write 8+5 (mod 12)≡1 or 8*5 (mod 12)≡4.

With negative values the same principle works, with the result depending on the sign of the modulus rather than the sign of the number or operation result. For example -3(mod 2)≡1 and -3(mod -2)≡-1. More generally, if *d* is the modulus and *n* is a number to be converted to its modular value, then the process can be viewed as an operation of the form: n-d*INT(n/d) where INT is a function that returns the Integer (whole number) part of the division n/d. Take our example of d=12 and n=8*5=40, we compute 40-12*INT(40/12)=40-12*INT(3+4/12) which is 40-36=4.

We can perform all of the usual arithmetic operations in a similar manner. For example, consider finding x, where $x=101^3$(mod 12). If we compute 101^3 we get 1030301 (interestingly a *palindrome number*, as it is the same written forwards or backwards). Then by division we obtain the result x=1030301(mod 12)≡5.

But we could have simplified this calculation by first evaluating 101(mod 12)≡5, and then finding 5^3=125(mod 12)≡5. Even more interesting is to observe that 101 (base10)=1100101 (base2, i.e. in binary). You can easily check this result using the Convert() function in Maple or Dec2Bin() in Excel. From earlier we know that this is the same as $2^6+2^5+2^2+2^0$, so our problem $x=101^3$(mod 12) can be re-written as

$x=2^6$(mod 12)+ 2^5(mod 12)+2^2(mod 12)+2^0(mod 12)

x=4+8+4+1=17(mod 12)≡5

This trick can also be applied to large exponents, enabling expressions such as m^e(mod n) where m and e are very large numbers to be computed very quickly and without the computer giving up (or overflowing). We will make use of this result in Part II.

It is quite reasonable to ask why we should be interested in such numbers and quirky arithmetic. The answer is that it has a surprising diversity of applications, a number of which we shall study in some detail in Part II. Amongst these are: ways in which data can be encrypted securely for transmission across the Internet; means of specifying the sequence number in a repeating series — for example, as part of the date field within Global Positioning System (GPS) devices, which use a modulus of 1024 for week identification; and procedures for generating random numbers.

I conclude with a couple of final observations about Integers, which are easy to state but have yet to be proved:

i.   every even number greater than 3 can be written as the sum of two primes (Goldbach's Conjecture, dating from 1742). So 28 can be written as 5+23 and 112 as 41+71 (unproven despite a $1million prize recently being offered for its solution)

ii.   every prime number greater than 3 is of the form 6n±1 for n=1, 2..., so 5=6-1 and 7=6+1, 127=6*21+1 etc. (all known Mersenne primes are of the form 6n+1)

5.2   Fractions (Rationals) and series

Rationals are numbers that can be written as a *ratio p/q*, where *p* and *q* are Integers and *q* is non-zero. If we permit *q*=±1 then we simply have the Integers, so in this sense the Integers are a subset of the Rationals. The set of all such numbers is sometimes denoted using the letter **Q**. All Rational numbers, expressed as decimals, have repeating digit sequences, although these may exhibit a long periodicity (require lots of digits before they repeat). If a Rational can be exactly represented as a decimal the repeating digits will be 0's, for example:

1/4=0.75000..., whereas
11/101=0.108910891089...

In this second example the infinite decimal representation shows a repeating pattern, or *periodicity*, which is an important feature of such numbers (I look at this characteristic again in Part II in connection with random number generation). The repeating pattern of decimal digits is sometimes marked by a horizontal bar, as noted earlier, called a *vinculum* from the Latin verb, to bind, e.g. $0.\overline{1089}$.

If we have a fraction *p/q*, *q*>1 and *p* is an Integer which is larger than *q* we can re-write this as *p*(1/*q*)=*pr* where *r*<1. However, if *p*<*q* then the fraction will already have a value 0<*r*<1. Thus all Rational numbers can be converted into a form that equates to values in the range 0<*r*<1. For example, if *p*=4 and *q*=2, we can write this as 4(1/2) and *r*=0.5; whilst 1/2, 2/4 and 4/8 are all separate fractions that have the same decimal value. The form 1/2 is not reducible any further and is known as the *irreducible* form of a rational. So some fractions are, in a sense, 'more likely' than others. If we calculate the value of all possible fractions starting with 1/2, 1/3, 2/3, 1/4, 2/4 etc. up to 199/200 there will be 200*199/2=19,900 different expressions. We can then produce a chart of how many times we get values like 0.5, 0.25 etc. (Figure 5.1). This chart shows that there is indeed a very distinctive pattern to the frequency of fractional values. This pattern would be repeated if we systematically examined a much larger number of possible fractions or if we randomly selected Integers *p* and *q* with *p*<*q* and then evaluated *p/q*.

A curious feature of this chart is that some fractional values do not occur at all or are relatively rare whilst the value 0.5 occurs roughly 100 times. If we zoom in on the area around 0.5 we see the pattern shown in Figure 5.2 (the thickness of the vertical lines is a minor, but important, distortion of the true pattern in these examples.

There are no fractions in our sample that give a value very close to 0.5. This is because we only considered Rational numbers with *q* up to 200, so the closest we can get to 1/2 is 99/199=0.49748... or 100/199=0.50251.... If we included values of *q* up to 400 we could get closer to 0.5 with 199/399=0.49874... and more generally we can see that between any two fractional

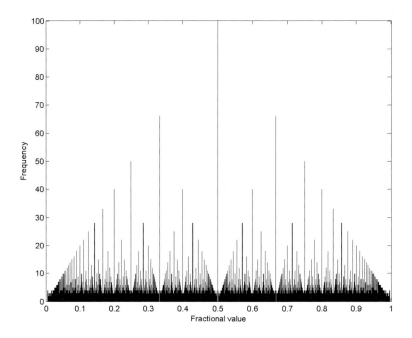

Figure 5.1 Frequency distribution of fractions

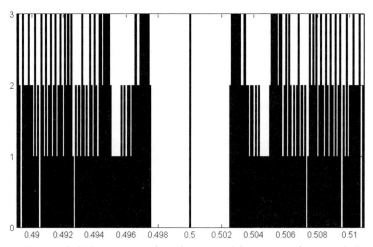

Figure 5.2 Frequency distribution of fractions close to 0.5

values (Rational numbers) we can always find another fraction, assuming we use a large enough value for q. So there are an infinite number of Rational numbers and it looks as though any gaps can always be filled. But, surprisingly, this is not the case. There are still gaps.

5.3   Irrationals and transcendentals

A number that cannot be expressed as a fraction or ratio is known as an Irrational. Irrational numbers can be expressed in decimal, binary or any number base, but in all instances they cannot be written down with a finite number of digits, only approximated. As an example, to provide final confirmation that such numbers do exist, consider the number 0.40400400040000... where at each stage we have added an extra 0 after the next occurrence of a 4. There is no periodicity in this decimal number, so it cannot be expressed as a fraction and is not therefore a Rational number. By implication, this number must somehow reside in a very small gap between Rational numbers.

There are some surprising conclusions we can draw as a result of these initial observations:

(i)   since Irrational numbers cannot be represented exactly using a finite number of decimal places, they can never be represented completely (numerically) within any computer system

(ii)   for every possible Rational number, x, there is an Irrational number, y say, that is just a tiny bit larger or smaller than x, and another Irrational number that is a tiny bit larger or smaller than y, z say, but which is still smaller than the 'next' Rational number. Since z cannot be represented as a Rational either, we can continue this idea to demonstrate (informally) that between every pair of Rational numbers there is an infinity of Irrational numbers (filling in all the possible gaps in our chart, Figure 5.1, no matter how large we make our divisor, q)

(iii)   since there appear to be many more Irrational numbers than Rational numbers, and these can never be represented exactly by a finite number of digits, we conclude that computers are unable to correctly represent the majority of numbers!

One of the first numbers proven to be Irrational was $n=\sqrt{2}$ (sometimes known as Pythagoras' constant), which in decimal is 1.414213562.... This number has special importance, as it can be regarded as the length of the diagonal of a square whose sides a each of length 1. The proof that $\sqrt{2}$ cannot be expressed as a fraction (is Irrational) is so simple I will provide it, just to show once more that Irrational numbers really do exist! I use the result that an odd number times an odd number gives an odd, whereas an even times an even or an odd gives an even. For example, 3*3=9, 3*7=21, 5*13=65 (all of which are odd), but 4*13=52 is even.

We start by assuming n can be written as a fraction, $n=a/b$, where a and b have no factors in common, i.e. this is the simplest possible fraction that can be written for n. Now $n=\sqrt{2}$ so $n^2=2$ and thus $a^2/b^2=2$, which means that $a^2=2b^2$. Thus a^2 is even and so a must be even from the observation I made earlier. Since a is even we can write $a=2c$, so from $a^2=2b^2$ we have $4c^2=2b^2$ so $2c^2=b^2$ and thus b must also be even. But if both a and b are even they have a common divisor, 2, which we said at the start was not the case, so we reach a contradiction. We conclude that we cannot write $n=a/b$, i.e. there is no fractional representation for $n=\sqrt{2}$. This argument can be extended in much the same way to show that the square root of all Integers that are not perfect squares are Irrational numbers. According to Greek legend, the philosopher Hippasus found the first proof that $\sqrt{2}$ could not be written as a fraction in around 500BC, but this result so distressed his fellow Pythagoreans that they threw him overboard from a ship to prevent the secret from becoming generally known.

I noted above that the number $\sqrt{2}$ arises as the diagonal of a square, with side length 1. We also know that this value times itself (squared) is equal to the sum of the squared values of the two sides, so $(\sqrt{2})^2=1^2+1^2$. This is actually a very simple form of equation, and could be written as $x^2=1^2+1^2$ or $x^2-2=0$, where x is the value we are trying to find. We have already shown that $\sqrt{2}$ cannot be written as a fraction, so is Irrational — now we have shown that it can be written as the solution to a simple equation with Integer coefficients (known more generally as an algebraic expression). *Transcendental numbers* are a subset of the Irrationals that cannot be written as the solution to such equations. They were so-named in the 18th century because they transcended this form of algebraic representation, but no numbers of this type were known (proven to be transcendental) at that time. It was not until the late 19th and early 20th centuries that proofs were found to show that both the constants π, and e (see further, Part III) were transcendental and that most Irrational numbers are transcendental. However, proving that specific numbers are transcendental has turned out to be extremely difficult and relatively few numbers are known for certain to be of this type.

5.4 Real numbers

The collection, or *set*, of all Rational numbers and all Irrational numbers is called the Real numbers and is usually denoted using the letter **R**. Sometimes this set is extended to include $-\infty$ and $+\infty$ and is denoted **R***. If only the positive Real numbers are considered then these are denoted **R⁺**. Real numbers (R*) are often described with reference to a straight line, extending from 0 upwards to plus infinity, and downwards through all the possible negative numbers to minus infinity (the *Real number line*):

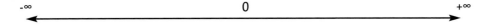

There are no gaps in this line, so we describe it as being continuous.

5.5 Imaginaries and complex numbers

Imaginary numbers are those involving negative square roots, i.e. numbers like $\pm\sqrt{-4}$, which can be written as $\pm 2\sqrt{-1}$. To avoid having to write the square root sign and -1 all the time, the shorthand form is to use the letter i (short for *Imaginary*) to represent such numbers, so we would write $2i$

for the square root of -4. If you have problems with the idea of negative numbers, as many people including mathematicians did until well into the 19th century, then square roots of negative numbers may seem even less comprehensible. But the first step is not to worry about what this means, rather simply accept that it may be useful to work with such numbers and see where this goes.

In the equation we had above, $x^2-2=0$, the solution is $x=\pm\sqrt{2}$. But what about $x^2+2=0$? In this case the solution should be $x=\pm\sqrt{-2}$, or $x=\pm(\sqrt{-1})\sqrt{2}=\pm i\sqrt{2}$, so even with very simple algebraic equations negative roots appear. With more complicated equations it turns out that Imaginaries may appear during the solution process, only to disappear at the end. This is because they may cancel themselves out during addition or multiplication, for example using the results $i \cdot i=0$, $i^* i=-1$, $-i^* \cdot i=-1$, $i^* \cdot i=1$.

So far so good. But what if the solution to a problem does not get rid of these imaginary values, and we are left we something like $3+4i$, or more generally $a+bi$? Well, we could regard this as a special kind of number, with a Real part and an Imaginary part, written for example as (a,b). With this in mind, instead of having just the Real number line, along which the Real part is located, we could have two separate lines or axes, one for the Real part and one for the Imaginary part, which together would describe a single point. This view of these composite values is given the name Complex Numbers, and the set of such numbers is often denoted C. It is not to indicate that they are especially complicated, more to show that they are rather different from the numbers we are used to.

Of course, once you introduce such numbers you need new definitions for the standard operations of addition, subtraction, multiplication and division. These definitions must be exactly the same as the ones we are used to if the Imaginary part is not there, so for addition we have the Complex number $(a,b)+(c,d)$ we get $(a+c,b+d)$. If b and d were both zero, we would be left with $a+c$, as one expects. The same happens with multiplication, but is a bit more complicated because sometimes we get $i^* i$ which gives us -1. So $(a+bi)^*(c+di)=(ac+adi+bci+bdi^2)=(ac-bd)+i(ad+bc)$, or $(ac-bd, ad+bc)$. From this we see that $(a+bi)^2=(a^2-b^2+i^2ab)$, a result that we will use in Part II. Again, if b and d were both zero we would be left with just the Real part, ac, as expected. Division of Complex numbers is also somewhat unfamiliar, with the expression $(a+bi)/(c+di)$ being evaluated by multiplying top and bottom by $(c-di)/(c-di)$, giving the rather unexpected result $(ac+bd)/(c^2+d^2)+i(bc-ad)/(c^2+d^2)$, which gives a/c if b and d are both 0.

Although Complex numbers look rather strange and appear to have little obvious use, they turn out to be extremely valuable in lots of practical fields. Many of these applications deal with problems that need to be considered in 2 dimensions rather than one. Examples include: understanding the smooth flow of fluids around obstacles, essential in the design of aircraft wings and turbines; modelling the behaviour of electric fields when designing equipment such as televisions and computer components; producing certain kinds of maps (such as the Transverse Mercator, used as the basis for the national map grids of many countries); and understanding the way in which heat is transferred.

5.6   Constants

The term Constant is usually reserved for interesting Real numbers that have a fixed value, as opposed to interesting Integers. There is a huge range of well known mathematical constants, but some of these occur so frequently in so many diverse fields that they warrant special attention. The two most famous and arguably important such constants are π and *e*. In addition, there are many important physical constants, sometimes referred to as Universal Constants. Examples of these include the speed of light, **c**, and the gravitational constant, **G**.

5.7   Infinities, large and small

"What's the greatest number you can think of?" said the Mathemagician. "Nine trillion, nine hundred and ninety-nine billion, nine hundred and ninety-nine million, nine hundred and ninety-nine," recited Milo breathlessly. "Very good" said the Mathemagician. "Now add one to it ... Now add one again." "But when can I stop?" pleaded Milo. "Never" said the Mathemagician with a little smile. Norman Juster, The Phantom Tollbooth, 1961

The concept of numerical infinity is both interesting and controversial. The common usage is that of a value which is bigger than any (by definition finite) number one cares to define. The symbol normally used to represent infinity is ∞, rather like a figure of 8 on its side — this symbol was originally used as an alternative to M, the Roman numeral 1000, but was changed in the 1600s by the English mathematician and cryptographer John Wallis to have its current meaning. In computer systems, which can only store a finite sized number, there tends to be at least three separate kinds of 'infinity'. The first is where a variable genuinely has no upper limit to its size, or possibly to the number of digits required to represent it. The second and very common instance, is where a 'divide by zero' operation occurs, often by accident, in which case the result is regarded as an error, undefined or nominally infinite. The third situation is what is known as an overflow, whereby a number is too large in some sense to be stored and the system fails in its attempt to deal with this situation. Strictly speaking the last two categories are not the usual context in which the term infinity is meant to apply.

Numerical infinity may be signed, i.e. positive or negative infinity, depending on which direction it is approached from, and some infinities may be 'larger' than others. This very curious concept is best explained with an example. The Integers, 1,2,3... etc. are clearly an infinite set — there is no upper limit to these. But the set is what we call *countable*, in that we can attempt to count every member of the set. We could also describe this as a (very large) set of *discrete* or distinct values. Between the number 1 and the number 2 there is an innumerable or *uncountable* number of Real numbers, and this is true for every interval, for example between 2 and 3, 3 and 4 etc. The set of Real numbers (and the set of Irrationals and transcendentals) are all much larger than the set of Integers. The notion of continuity, by which we mean the existence of a *continuous* set of values, may be considered as being equivalent to the definition of the Real number line.

Between the number 1 and the number 2 there is also an apparently unlimited number of fractional (Rational) numbers, such as 2/3, 3/4, 4/5 etc., and likewise between 2 and 3, and so forth. So there appears to be far more Rationals than Integers — Rationals seem to represent a larger infinity than Integers. However, it turns out the set of all Rationals is still *countable*, by which is meant that we can associate an Integer in the sequence 1,2,3,... etc. to every fraction, and thus in this sense the set of all Integers and the set of all Rationals are regarded as being of the same size.

Are there smaller infinite sets than the Integers? Again, the answer to this appears to be yes, since sets like "all even numbers" or "all odd numbers" have far fewer members (half the number?). However, just like the set of all fractions, such sets are countable, so are the same 'size' as the set of Integers.

An infinite set with far fewer members still is the set of "all prime numbers". Around 2500 years ago Euclid presented a simple proof that this set is not finite, so the concept is far from modern. He observed that the number $q=2*3*5*7*...*p+1$ formed by multiplying all the prime numbers less than or equal to a prime number p together, and then adding 1, is not divisible by any of these smaller primes, so must itself be prime. We can continue this process now using q, and thus generate an unlimited number of ever-larger prime numbers — at least in theory. In practice to do this we would have to know the value of every prime number up to and including p, and then q, to perform this calculation, which in general we do not. But it is the logic of the argument that matters here, not how practical it would be to carry out the operation!

We tend to think of infinite values and sets in terms of very large numbers or collections of objects. However, we also use the term infinite in the context of vanishingly small numbers, or *infinitesimal* values, numbers that approach the value of 0 to an arbitrary degree. Such values occur in many situations, for example when calculating the sum of an infinite series or computations that involve analysing rates of change or computing the area inside a curved boundary. For example, as n increases in size, $1/n$ becomes smaller and smaller. We can see that eventually $1/n$ will become as close as we like to 0, but if we examine this using our computer there will be a value of n for which this process fails or becomes very unreliable. A similar problem occurs with any very small quantity, for example small angles. A distance on the Earth's surface of 10 metres, for example, is approximately one millionth of the distance from the equator to the pole, as we saw earlier. This quarter section of the Earth's surface extends over a range of 90 degrees, so our

10 metres equates to one millionth of 90 degrees, or to 0 degrees, 0 minutes and 0.0000900... seconds – a very small angle indeed. Trigonometric functions, such as sin() and cos() of such very small angles are very close to 0 and 1 respectively. In fact, by the time we get to considering a surface distance of 10cms, the cos() function in Microsoft's Excel gives up and always displays the result as 1.0000.... This result occurs either because the computer cannot store enough digits to correctly represent very large or very small numbers, or because when it tries to calculate a function or expression it fails in some way – this may or may not result in an error message or warning, depending on the circumstances and software involved. This is distinct from the rounding issue I have previously described, where an answer *displayed* as 1.0000 could simply be the result of rounding up for display a number like 0.99998.

5.8   Random numbers and frequency diagrams

It is possible to create Real numbers or sets of Real numbers that are regarded as *random*. By this is meant that the chance of any particular number in a given range being created or selected is identical to that of any other number in that range. For example, with a 6-sided die, we expect the numbers 1, 2, 3, 4, 5, and 6 all to be rolled with equal frequency if the die is true and no tricks are played by the person rolling the die. The same applies for a roulette wheel, a coin being tossed or a completely shuffled pack of cards (although in this last case each of the card face values will arise 4 times in 52 or 1 in 13). In practice this does not happen – if we keep rolling a die or spinning the roulette wheel each value will appear a certain number of times (with a given *frequency*) which will tend to show an even distribution of frequencies, but will not be exactly even. Likewise, computer systems will often provide 'random numbers' which are generated according to an algorithm with nearly equal frequency behaviour, but in this case the numbers are not truly random. Such numbers are called pseudo-random, and are often generated for the interval [0,1]. So, for example, in Excel if you enter =rand() into a cell, a random number like 0.3419 will be displayed. If you create a row or column with =rand() in each cell, a series of different values will be created. New random numbers are produced whenever the spreadsheet is re-calculated or if the function key F9 is pressed. Most computer software packages offer such facilities, and pseudo-random numbers in any range can be generated by multiplying the results provided by an appropriate expression or value. In Excel's case there are known problems with some versions of its random number generation (e.g. in some implementations for Macintosh computers), so over-reliance on the numbers generated is not recommended. If in doubt, for a project that relies heavily on the quality of computer generated random numbers, large test sets should be created and their quality examined carefully.

However, for many purposes facilities in programs such as Excel will be fine, so I will use these in several of the examples that follow. Using Excel I filled 40 columns from rows 1 to 20 with random numbers, each cell containing =rand()*10. I then took the average value in each column, i.e. the

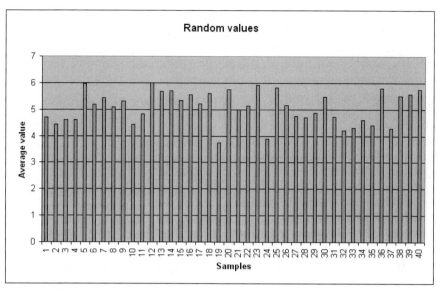

Figure 5.3 Random numbers, average values in range 0-10

average of the 20 values in that column, by dividing each column total by 20. The results are shown in Figure 5.3. We would expect the average (i.e. arithmetic mean value) to be 5.0. However, as can be seen from Figure 5.3 (which shows the mean values for each of the 40 columns) it varies from under 4 to 6.

The actual pattern of frequencies in this case can be seen by counting the number of values generated in the ranges 0-1, >1-2, >2-3 etc. up to >9-10. This grouping of values is a form of classification of our results into 10 categories that we shall number 1 to 10. We can plot these categories as a bar chart showing frequencies rather than values (Figure 5.4), and this form of chart is called a histogram (from the Greek, *histos*, a mast).

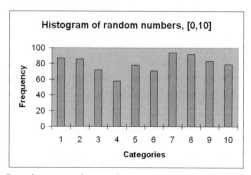

Figure 5.4 Random numbers, frequency of values in range 0-10

This chart shows that with 800 randomly generated numbers in the range [0,10] roughly 80 will be found in each unit interval, but there is variation in these frequencies. The bars in this chart all have the same width, because each interval is 1 unit. This is the normal arrangement, but if the intervals are not equal the widths should reflect this, in proportion.

Because these numbers are program-generated there is a risk that the same set of 'random' numbers will be created next time you use the spreadsheet or run the program, so in a sense these would no longer be random. The usual solution to this is to allow you to specify a different start value (or *seed*) each time the function is called — often the number of seconds or milliseconds recorded by the computer since midnight is used for this purpose. Other computer-related variables that are often used in the generation of random numbers include: the current date-time in milliseconds; the current system status; and the current system memory usage. Interactive programs, such as those that use Microsoft Windows or X-Windows interfaces, may utilise the sequence and timing of recent keystrokes or mouse movements as part of their seed selection process. A simple algorithm for generating pseudo-random numbers is provided in Part II.

If we examine the frequency pattern of the average values from a large number of samples of 20 random numbers in the range [0,10] we obtain a remarkable result. Instead of finding an even pattern of averages, we see that most of the values are close to the expected average of 5, with fewer results being found as we look above and below this value (see Figure 5.5). The chart shows the number of averaged values, in a sample of just over 250 sets of data, in evenly spaced ranges (the upper boundary of the ranges are shown). What is even more extraordinary is that this kind of pattern is found whenever large independent random samples are obtained from any under-lying pattern, not just one where all the values are equally likely, or uniform.

Taking averages of measured datasets changes the data into a well-defined and well-understood pattern of the kind we have just seen. This new pattern tends to be the shape of a bell, and is

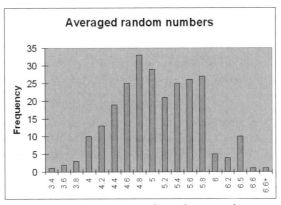

Figure 5.5 Averages of random numbers

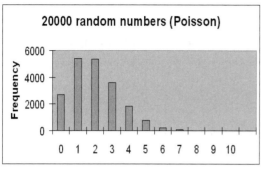 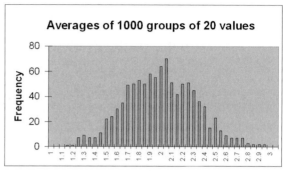

Figure 5.6 Random numbers and the central limit theorem

known as the Normal Distribution. The fact that datasets exhibit this property when averages are taken is known as the *central limit theorem*, and is one of the most important discoveries in the history of mathematics and statistics.

I can tell you don't believe the previous statement, so here is an example (see the two histograms, Figure 5.6). Again, these have been created using random numbers generated by Excel, but in this case we created 20 columns of 1000 random numbers using a non-uniform pattern known as the Poisson distribution (named after the French mathematician, Siméon-Denis Poisson, not after the French for fish). The result is a set of random numbers, 0,1,2,3..., with a mean value of 2, for which the frequencies are far from regular — lower values such as 1 or 2 are much more likely than values of 5 or above. The average spread (standard deviation) for the Poisson is √mean so √2 in this case, i.e. about 1.414...

Now, when we add across the 20 columns and take the 1000 average values, the result is a bell-shaped frequency pattern again, despite the fact that the initial distribution is no longer uniform. What is more, the new distribution has the same mean as the original distribution (i.e. 2) and we can see that the spread is much smaller — only ranging from 1 to 3. This reduction in spread always happens when we apply averaging in this way, and if s is the average spread of the original distribution then s/√n is the average spread in the new distribution, where n is the number of values used in the averaging process. In our example n=20, so the average spread should be around 0.316, and in fact was 0.321. All of the figures and diagrams in these examples can be created within Excel using the Tools menu, Data Analysis option (you may need to install the Analysis ToolPak add-in via the Tools, Add-ins menu to enable this option).

6 DATA

I have used the term *data* in many contexts so far, without examining it more closely. Data is the term used to refer to a specific set of information, often but not always numeric, collected from the world around us. As such, the collection and measurement methods involved are a central part of understanding data. By its very nature, data tends to be inexact, either because it relates to something very complex in the real world which we can only partially understand and model, or because the process and timing of measurement itself is subject to error. As with Chapter 2, readers familiar with the basics of data types and data analysis may wish simply to glance through this short chapter and then proceed to Chapter 7, which deals with the notion of dimension.

If you have any doubts about these ideas, here are descriptions of four Myths about the data relating to maps and map-making, as explained by the Ordnance Survey, who are responsible for the production of all official maps in the UK:

Myth 1. A point on the ground has a unique latitude and longitude:
"... different systems of latitude and longitude in common use today can disagree on the coordinates of a point by more than 200 metres. For any application where an error of this size would be significant, it's important to know which system is being used and exactly how it is defined."

Myth 2. A horizontal plane is a level surface
"Of course it cannot be, because the Earth is round — any gravitationally level surface (such as the surface of the wine in your glass, or the surface of the sea averaged over time) must curve as the Earth curves, so it cannot be flat (that is, it cannot be a geometrical plane)... When we say 'a level surface' we mean a surface which is every-where at right angles to the direction of gravity. The direction of gravity is generally towards the centre of the Earth as you would expect, but it varies in direction and magnitude from place to place in a complex way, even on a very local scale."

Myth 3. The true coordinates of a ground point never change
"They certainly do, due to the continuous deforming motions of the Earth. Relative to the centre of the Earth, a point on the ground can move as much as a metre up and down every day just because of the tidal influences of the Sun and Moon. The relative motion of two continents can be 10 centimetres a year, which is significant for mapping because it is constant year after year — after 50 years a region of the Earth may have moved by 5 metres relative to a neighbouring continent."

Myth 4. There are exact mathematical formulas to change between coordinate systems
"Exact formulas only apply in the realm of perfect geometry — not in the real world of coordinated points on the ground. The 'known coordinates' of a point in one coordinate system are obtained from a large number of observations which are averaged together

using a whole raft of assumptions. Both the observations and the assumptions are only ever approximately correct and can be of dubious quality, particularly if the point was coordinated a long time ago. It will also have moved since it was coordinated, due to subsidence, continental plate motion and other effects."

In some instances (notably for data collected by some national and international agencies) datasets are accompanied by a considerable amount of explanatory information, which is effectively data about data, or *metadata*. There are now agreed standards for the format and content of metadata, and even if a given dataset is not provided with such information, it is worth examining the topics that one would expect to be included in order to understand the quality of the information you have. The key point about data, then, is that it is always approximate, always a snapshot and model of the real world, and we must accept and appreciate this whenever working with such information.

6.1   Summarising data

Numerical datasets can be characterised or summarised using a wide variety of measures. One can note how many items there are (the *count*), what are the largest (*maximum*) and smallest (*minimum*) values (the extremes), and what is the *range* of values (simply the difference between the maximum and minimum). Extreme values do not give a very good picture of many datasets, since it could be that they are one-off values, nothing like most of the values, maybe as a result of errors. For this reason one often works with the *average* or *mean* value, calculated by simply adding all values and dividing by the number of values in the dataset. Another commonly used measure is the *median*, or middle value, which is found by arranging all the values in numerical order and then taking the middle value or the average of the two middle values if there are an even number of values. These simple measures also give a very limited view so often it is useful to provide some measure of the *variation* in the data, for example the average variation or the range of values that lie not too far from the mean. Collectively such measures are known as *basic statistics*.

6.2   Scales and Classification

Where a dataset contains many numbers it is often useful to group these into classes and then show the results in a table or on a chart or diagram. Grouping in this way is a form of classification, and is often as much an art as a science. It is also highly dependent on the kind of data that you are working on. I start by explaining the main types or scales of numerical data that commonly arise.

6.2.1 Data scales
Where the data describes collections that are pre-defined by named groupings (*Nominal* data),

e.g. sheep, cattle and pigs; or Republicans, Democrats and Other parties; or even "Numbers", "Letters" and "Other symbols"; then these groupings will form the basis for classification. In these examples there is still plenty of scope for errors, misclassification and uncertainty, but the classes essentially define themselves.

Data that is arranged in a numeric or alphabetic order, but is otherwise essentially Nominal in character, is called *Ordinal* data. Examples of ordinal data are groups of patients who are in Stage 1, Stage 2 or Stage 3 of a disease, or popularity ratings that are High, Medium or Low. In general such data will have distinct categories and these predefine the grouping or classification, with the proviso that the ordering must be preserved. Simple numerical relational operations are permitted: for example =, <, > and ≠ (not equal to). Where the categories are less well-defined, selection of classes remains an issue. For example, in a colour sensitivity test there may be 30 blocks of colour from blue through various shades of purple to red. There is an order here, and when the results of the test are collected one might seek to group the data into 5 categories: blue, blue purple, purple, red purple and red. The order is preserved but we have chosen a particular grouping of the data that differs from the original 30-group arrangement.

Interval data means that we have a set of values, e.g. temperature readings (positive, negative or zero) that we can use in numerical operations (like calculating differences), but it is not meaningful to use these in calculations that involve ratios. For example, 30 degrees Celsius is not twice as hot as 15 degrees Celsius. The scales for Celsius and Fahrenheit do not have a *meaningful* zero value in this sense. However, it is valid to calculate and compare intervals or differences on these scales, so $37°-36°=28°-27°$ is correct for both of these scales. More generally, if x is an interval scale variable then operations such as $3x-2x\equiv2x-x$ are valid. An example of a scale that looks rather like an interval or ordinal scale but is neither, is a questionnaire answer with options 1=low, 2=medium, 3=high, 4=don't know. The last item is clearly not part of an ordered set, nor are the numbers assigned to answers part of a well-defined scale with regular (equal) intervals — this is a Nominal scale.

If you want to compute *ratios* on temperature data you need to use the Kelvin scale, for which it is correct to say that 30 degrees Kelvin is twice as hot as 15 degrees Kelvin, since these are measures of thermal energy, with absolute zero (0°K=-273.16°C) being the point at which there is no thermal energy at all.

If the five colours in our earlier example were defined by known proportions of red (100%, 75%, 50%, 25%, 0%) in a pure red-blue mix, equally spaced as previously described, the grouping would conform to *interval* scaling. In this case it is correct to say that the difference between group 3 and group 4 in terms of red component is 50%-25%=25%. It is also correct to say that group 3 has twice as much red component as group 4 (50%/25%), which is a ratio. So this example is also a *ratio* scale — it has a meaningful 0, in this case "no red". This process demonstrates that with careful design, a data collection exercise that might have been limited to purely nominal scaled

Table 6-1 Richter scale of earthquake magnitude

Descriptor	Richter magnitudes	Earthquake Effects	Frequency of Occurrence (estimated global)
Micro	< 2.0	Micro earthquakes, not felt	8,000 per day
Very minor	2.0-2.9	Generally not felt, but recorded	1,000 per day
Minor	3.0-3.9	Often felt, but rarely causes damage	50,000 per year
Light	4.0-4.9	Noticeable shaking of indoor items, rattling noises. Significant damage unlikely	6,000 per year
Moderate	5.0-5.9	Can cause major damage to poorly constructed buildings over small regions. At most slight damage to well-designed buildings	800 per year
Strong	6.0-6.9	Can be destructive in areas up to about 100 miles across in populated areas	120 per year
Major	7.0-7.9	Can cause serious damage over larger areas	18 per year
Great	8.0-8.9	Can cause serious damage in areas several hundred miles across	1 per year
Rare Great	9.0+		1 per 20 years

results (counts by category) can be transformed into one which has interval or ratio properties, facilitating much more sophisticated analysis. Thorough planning and design in the initial stages of any experiment or project that involves data collection reaps many rewards in the later stages.

6.2.2 Special scales
As with temperature, in many different application areas there are specially designed scales that have come into widespread usage. For example, the recent devastating tsunami in the Indian Ocean was triggered by a "magnitude 9.3" sub-sea earthquake event. The value 9.3 refers to the Richter scale (Table 6-1), introduced in 1935. This is a base10 logarithmic ratio scale. By this we mean that earthquakes that cause seismic movements of roughly 1, 10, 100, 1000, 10000... units are categorised as having Richter magnitude values of 0, 1, 2, 3, 4... so that a magnitude 9 event is 10,000 times as powerful as a typical moderate (5 magnitude) earthquake.

By contrast, the scale invented by Friedrich Mohs in 1812 to measure the relative hardness of mineral substances is strictly ordinal (Table 6-2).

This scale has largely arbitrary values 1...10 based on whether substances can scratch one another. As can be seen from the third column, the scale is far from being even (the latter values are based on Mohs' ideas but using modern equipment to provide absolute hardness values).

6.2.3 Numerical classification
Classification issues arise most frequently with interval or ratio data, especially when we have a

Table 6-2 Mohs hardness scale

Substance	Value	Absolute hardness
Diamond	10	1500
Corundum	9	400
Topaz	8	200
Quartz	7	100
Orthoclase (Feldspar)	6	72
Aptite	5	48
Fluorite	4	21
Calcite	3	9
Gypsum	2	3
Talc	1	1

large quantity of information to summarise. These have similarities with the problems of statistical grouping and zoning that we described at the very start of this book. Assuming that you have a set of such data, there are a very wide range of methods that you may adopt for grouping the information, but we will restrict our discussion to some of the most widely used. There are two central issues:

• how many groups do I want? and
• how shall I decide which values go into which groups?

How many groups? There is no definitive answer to this, depending as it does on the volume of data one has, what analysis of the data is to be performed, how much loss of information there will be when information is grouped, and how the data is to be communicated to others. If there is a very large number of categories the number of data items in each category will generally be small or zero, whilst with only one category all the data will be in this and there will be no information about the pattern of variation. Very often using an odd number of categories, between 5 and 11, provides a balance between loss of detail and identification of pattern, in a manner that is readily understood in diagrams, charts, maps and so forth. As a general rule, if possible, class boundaries should not correspond to actual data values (i.e. data should lie within distinct classes rather than on the boundary) and, where possible, well within (e.g. close to the mid value of the class).

To illustrate some of these ideas we will use the set of data collected as part of Michelson's experiment carried out in 1879 to determine the speed of light. The data is a set of 100 values for the speed of light, estimated by taking very careful measurements over a 28-day period. Each value is actually the average of a set of measurements. In this example we are looking at one main variable, the measured speed of light. The values recorded range from 299.62 to 300.07 thousand kilometres per second. If we vary the number of classes, and use equal spacing, we can see the effect of this on a simple frequency plot (or bar chart) of the data (Figure 6.1). The leftmost chart shows the actual observations, many of which were recorded as the same speed values, and the rightmost chart shows this dated grouped into 5 classes, with the x-axis showing the class upper-boundaries (in 000km/s). Our choice of the number of classes here is arbitrary and clearly poor in this case. The class boundaries have been pre-defined to include all the data values with evenly spaced rounded values (a more useful 9-class example was previously shown in Figure 3.11). The width of the vertical bars is also somewhat arbitrary, but in the examples shown should be constant. There is also a debate as to whether the bars should touch or have gaps between them. There is no strict rule on this, although often separate bars are used to indicate data that can only take discrete values, such as -1, 0, 1, 2... whilst bars that have no gaps indicate data that can take any values in a continuous range. In this book I have used separate bars everywhere, purely for simplicity!

Other choices could be made for the number of classes and class boundaries based on closer examination of the data. A widely used approach is to divide the data such that a fixed percentage lies in each class. To do this the values are first placed in ascending order. With 100 values the first 25 will be in the first 25% and so forth. If the categories are set at, say, 0%-25%, 25.01%-50%, 50.01%-75% and 75.01%-100% we have four classes each of which contains a quarter of the data (or as close to 25% as possible), and these are called *quartiles*. The class boundaries in our case will be unequal: [299.62-299.80], [299.81-299.85], [299.86-299.89] and [299.90-300.07], so the class widths (and bar widths if we plot the data) vary substantially. All these four classes have equal frequencies, with 50% of all the results falling in the range [299.81-299.89] — this middle range is called the *inter-quartile range* (IQR) as it includes the values that fall between the 25th and 75th percentile (percentile is used to indicate each frequency percentage point of a set of values arranged in ascending order).

Another, widely used approach for classifying data of this type is to examine the pattern of data variation either side of the average or mean value. Our dataset has a mean of 299.85 and if we

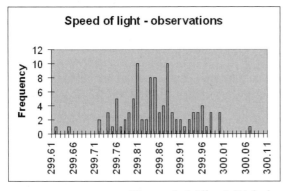 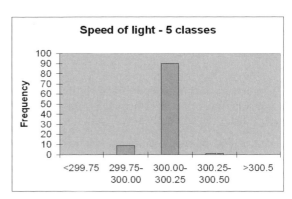

Figure 6.1 Albert Michelson's speed of light data, 1879

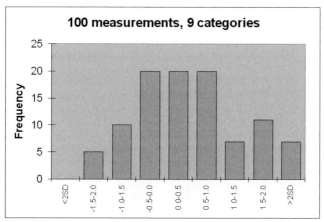

Figure 6.2 Categorisation by standard deviations from the mean

divide the range (maximum value minus minimum value) into 9 classes each class has a width of 0.225 units. But most of the data is clustered around the mean value, with an average difference from the mean of only 0.08 units (the average difference in this case is known as the *standard deviation* or SD for short — see Appendix 1 for more details). So perhaps it would be more helpful to set our class boundaries at the mean ±0.04 units (i.e. ±0.5SDs), ±0.08, ±0.12 and ±0.16 or more units (i.e. >±2SDs, as illustrated in Figure 6.2).

Leaving the first and last categories open-ended in this way reduces the problem of our class boundaries being badly affected by a few rogue values (*outliers*), which might be data errors or be unusual values that require separate examination and explanation.

The number of classes, coupled with the range or other measures of spread, determines the class boundaries, and hence which values go into which class. But there may be other factors than the data values themselves that need to be considered. In this particular dataset the air temperature was recorded for each set of measurements. Instead of grouping the results by value, we could group the measurements according to the temperature ranges involved, and examine the average speed values recorded in each category. The frequencies shown by the grey bars in Figure 6.3 are now the number of measurements in each range and the black diamonds indicate the average values recorded in these cases, with its scale on the right hand side. A 'best fit' line has been added to this chart to highlight the fact that there appears to be a trend in the data, suggesting that the speed of light in air increases with temperature or, more likely in this case, the meas-urement process was affected in some way by the ambient temperature.

6.2.4 Classification with multiple variables

The preceding examples focused on a single main variable (measurements of the speed of light) although towards the end of the discussion we have introduced a second variable, the ambient

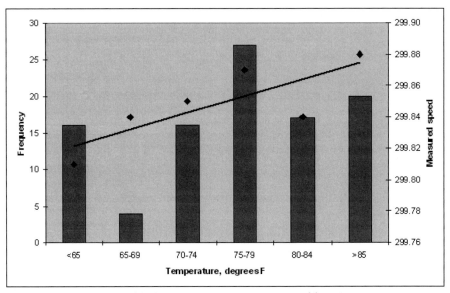

Figure 6.3 Speed of light measurements, grouped by air temperature

temperature recorded during these measurements. When the data to be classified incorporates values for samples (e.g. soil samples) on which several measurements, **m**, have been made (proportion of sand, concentration of certain chemicals, moisture content etc.) then classification methods must be extended to incorporate these different factors. A common procedure is to group together those samples that are most similar to each other and as distinct as possible from other samples. There are many methods for achieving such groupings. A common procedure is to view each set of **m** measurements as a point in m-dimensional space and then these points are searched to see how many clusters can be identified, such that some pre-defined criteria are satisfied. Examples of criteria include: that each sample must be assigned to just one cluster or group; no sample may be more than a certain 'distance' from other members of the group or the nominal central point in m-space that represents the group average; every group centre must be separated from every other group centre by a certain amount; etc. Collectively such procedures are known as multi-variate clustering techniques.

7 DIMENSION

7.1   Integer dimensions

As I noted earlier, Real numbers (R*) are often described with reference to a straight line, extending from 0 upwards to plus infinity, and downwards through all the possible negative numbers to minus infinity. This arrangement gives us one *dimension*. A single point on this line is regarded as having no dimension, or dimension of 0. If we wish to refer to a point on this line in general terms, rather than a specific point, we tend to use the symbol x, to indicate that this is some unspecified value or 'variable'.

We learnt at school that if we arrange a second line, (usually) at right angles to the first, we can describe the position of any point on this plane using values, or *coordinates*, determined by the values on each of these two distinct lines or axes. So a point in 2 dimensions (2D) on a plane surface can be described by referring to a pair of values or coordinates, say (x,y). We are familiar with this representation having a physical interpretation, like points on a table surface or in a field, but there is no reason we should not use this idea for other purposes. For example, later in our discussion, we will be looking at changes of population numbers, p, with time, t, and in such cases we can record this using the pairs (p,t) as a set of points or line(s) in 2D space (a scatter plot or line graph). Likewise, we may have two inter-related populations, P and Q, and be interested in examining the possible values of both of these under a variety of conditions, which again we may choose to plot in 2D (see further, Part II).

If we extend a third line, at right angles to the first two, we create a box-like set of lines giving us a way of representing points in 3 dimensions (as illustrated earlier when discussing vectors and colour space). We represent points in this 3 dimensional space using separate variables or values for each coordinate, for example (1,2.5,40) or (x,y,z). Then we were introduced to time as a fourth dimension, represented by (x,y,z,t) and more recently there have been all sorts of discussions about higher dimensions, strings and super-strings, 11-dimensional space (the usual 4 plus 7 more!), parallel universes and much more that is very difficult to comprehend. What we do know is that our experiences suggest that the 1,2 and 3-dimensional view of the world is a pretty good one and seems to work well for most purposes. The number of dimensions appears to be explained using whole numbers and zero (for a single point).

But is this correct and sufficient? This representation using numbers or variables turns a highly visual, complex geometric world into a form suitable for algebraic manipulation, and enables you to ignore the visual models. This is a very powerful and successful idea, but it turns out to have limitations. Some of these issues have only come to light relatively recently, in many cases following the use of computers as a tool for experimentation and visualisation.

7.2   Fractional dimensions

One issue that often arises is that we can often only measure the value of a third variable or 'dimension' at a selection of points (e.g. over a regular grid of points) in 2D. This occurs when landscape height is measured at regular intervals or regular samples of any variable such as rock type or environmental radioactivity are taken. In this case we have an idea of a 3D representation but only at fixed points, and such datasets are often described as having two and one half dimensions, or 2.5D. Of course, the same is true in many situations where values of one variable, e.g. air temperature, are only known for fixed intervals against another variable, e.g. time or altitude, so for these cases we might use the term 1.5D, but this is less common. This usage is largely a matter of language and communication of ideas, rather than indicating that the underlying data has a non-Integer dimension — it is still assumed that it is theoretically possible to fill in all the gaps and obtain a true 2D or 3D dataset if enough time and money were available to do the research (unless the data in question are not continuous, e.g. counts of distinct items).

However, in the late 19th century cracks began to appear in the idea that dimensions only came in whole numbers. The theories and proofs involved are often quite complicated, but one or two examples serve to illustrate the difficulties. The first is "how long is a piece of string?" (or coastline, national border etc.). A mathematical line is, strictly speaking, a *model* of a piece of string — the string itself actually is much more complicated, consisting of twisted fibres, linked together to form a long thin structure. When we measure a piece of string we usually resort to stretching it out so it is as straight as possible, marking where the ends reach, and then using a ruler or similar device to measure the gap — this assumes the string is a perfect linear, non-stretchy object between the two ends and our ruler and measurement process is perfect — for many practical purposes this is good enough. But if we marked a point about half way along the string as well as the two ends it is likely that the two sections we measure will total a slightly greater length than the first measurement we made. This is due to the imperfect nature of the string — it is not perfectly straight and is fibrous. It turns out that if we repeat this process, using smaller and smaller steps, down to even microscopic levels, the string appears to get longer and longer in terms of the total length we are recording. In fact it can appear to be enormously long. This is not what we were told by our mathematics teacher in high school.

If something that appears to be linear can be almost any length you wish, it starts to undermine one's confidence. This problem came into sharp focus when a scientist named L F Richardson started to examine the lengths of national boundaries in the 1930s. He was interested to see if countries that had long boundaries with their neighbours were more prone to having disputes and conflicts than those with short borders. What he found, as a side effect of this work, was that the length of borders depended on the level of detail shown on the maps he was using, and of course, how he measured these lengths once he had a map. In this case, the maps were already a form of model of the real world, but he would have experienced a similar result if he had been surveying or pacing out the borders on the ground.

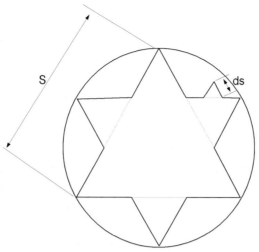

Figure 7.1 Construction of the Koch snowflake

These strange results are actually the norm, because whenever we measure the real (physical) world (collecting data) we are assuming a particular model applies, and that specific measuring processes are to be carried out. When we measure the area of a field we generally assume it is perfectly flat, with clearly defined borders. In fact fields are nothing like this close up, they are neither flat, very well defined, nor are their surfaces perfectly smooth. They are infinitely complex structures when looked at closely, and taking account of this intricacy a field may be as large as you wish. This is highly unsatisfactory!

Even within the world of idealised mathematical lines and regions, some nasty problems were being discovered. For example, researchers found a way of drawing a very wiggly line around a field, such that the line was infinitely long but the field's area was finite (Figure 7.1). In this example, discovered by Helge von Koch in 1904, you start by drawing a triangle with all sides having equal length. Then you divide each side into three, remove the middle third, and use it to construct a new triangle (with no base) on the side you have selected. This process can be indefinitely repeated, and the total length of the boundary grows without limit. However, the 'snowflake' does not grow beyond the enclosing circle shown, so must have a finite area.

Mathematicians also discovered that another very wiggly line could be drawn inside a square boundary, such that the line passed through every single point inside the square — so in some senses lines (1-dimensional objects) and areas (2-dimensional objects) could be regarded as having the same dimension.

Most of these real-world and theoretical issues occur when we have what is called recursion or self-similarity in our data. Recursion means that the same rule is applied over and over again, starting with an initial object or set of data and then re-applying the same rule to the resulting output values. Self-similarity means that when you examine an object more closely, as if with a magnifying glass or microscope, it appears similar to larger pieces of the object, no matter how closely you observe it. Self-similarity can be created from recursive processes, amongst others. If this pattern shows similarity across a wide range of scales or all scales, it has been described as having a fractional dimension — many complex linear-type objects are found to have a dimension of between 1 and 2. This is the origin of the term *fractals*, studied and popularised from the 1960s onwards by the mathematician and scientist, Beniot Mandelbrot (see also Section 13.2 entitled Recursion and Chaos in Part II of this book). A revised view of many real-world datasets, covering an enormous range of disciplines, has been one in which fractals seem to be everywhere: in cloud patterns; in stock market price fluctuations; in the way in which cells grow and divide; in music and art; in physics and electronics; and, incidentally, on the covers of this book.

The formal definition of dimension was extended in the late 19th and early 20th centuries to incorporate these 'less obvious' objects by extending the idea of filling up a region — calculating the number of small basic units or building blocks required to completely fill or cover the space one is examining. So with a simple line, we need lots of little strips of length S, say, to completely cover the line. With a field we need lots of little squares, of area S^2 say, to cover the space. With a volume we need lots of little cubes, of volume S^3 to fill the space. The thing to notice here is that the exponent goes up regular steps 1,2,3... With fractals we find that the exponent goes up in fractional amounts, so we regard some lines as having dimension between 1 and 2 and some surfaces as having dimension between 2 and 3. If an object has a fractal dimension of 1.7, say, it does not tell us how it was produced, just that it is an intermediate kind of object, more than a line and not quite an area. The general term for dimensions defined using this coverage approach is *capacity* dimension.

7.3   Topology and dimension

Human vision "... should be divided into two classes, primitive and learned. Those such as Euclidean straightness, parallelism and the like are learned, while such factors as contiguity, boundary and closedness [topological factors] are probably primitive" Profs. Fred Roberts and Patrick Suppes, 1967, in an article in the academic journal 'Synthese'.

Topology can be thought of as the study of spatial relationships without reference to distance measurements. It is concerned with examining the fundamental characteristics of objects such as lines and surfaces in terms of their connectedness and continuity: whether they have holes in them; how one surface (say a cube) might be stretched like rubber to produce the shape of a football; and what happens when we cut these objects in different ways? Perhaps topology can provide a different insight into the notion of dimension?

Instead of looking at dimensions in terms of sets of Real numbers we can try a topological perspective. I noted earlier that a point has dimension 0, and a line has dimension 1. A line can be divided into two separate parts by a point — maybe this provides a clue to dimensionality? Extending the idea further, we see that a line will divide or cut an area into two, and a plane will divide or cut a volume into two. We could use these observations to help us define 1-, 2- and higher-dimensional space. Introducing cuts focuses attention on how objects are connected — cutting an object — line, surface etc., breaks it up and changes its degree of connectedness (its *topology*), rather than being concerned with the object's size or extent in particular directions. This notion is more basic and in some ways, more meaningful, than abstract notions of dimensionality. It can also be more revealing.

In the late 19th and early 20th centuries some forms of lines (knots) and surfaces (donuts, paper strips, bottles) were discovered that were best characterised by their connectivity rather than attempting a description or definition using traditional models. For example, consider an object like the Earth or the Moon. These are sphere-like objects with a single closed surface. If you draw a circle or oval on the surface of such a figure it divides the surface into two distinct parts (Figure 7.2A) — the surface of all sphere-like objects can be regarded as having two dimensions. Notice that there is no real concept of inside and outside this circle, there are two 'insides' depending on which way you are facing (this is perhaps more obvious for a sphere if your initial circle extends right around the equator). In fact the idea of *inside* really needs a definition of its own, something like "if you walk clockwise around the edge of a figure, the area to your right is defined as inside". So *inside* is a relative concept, not an absolute. Finally, notice that the evenly spaced grid on this sphere results in a pattern of small regions (lines of latitude and longitude in the context of the Earth) that cover the globe. The size of these regions near the poles is far less than at the equator — in fact at the poles these regions become vanishingly small. This is an important observation I will discuss later in this book.

A shape that looks a bit like a sphere at first sight, but which is quite different and has many important applications, is the torus (Figure 7.2B). Also known as the donut (or ring doughnut), this is essentially a sphere with a hole in it so it becomes ring shaped (more than one hole is possible, but we shall stick to the simplest case). In the case of a single-holed torus (a *one-fold* torus) there are two quite distinct circles that can be drawn on the surface to divide the figure — one circle can be drawn on the surface, broadly in the horizontal plane, and another can be drawn in broadly the vertical plane, as indicated by the two sets of grid lines. Each slices the torus, the first being broadly into a top and bottom, whilst the second separates the torus into a long sausage-like shape. From our cutting rule we still say that the surface of a torus is two dimensional, but has greater (more complex) connectivity than the sphere.

Donut shapes are not simply for eating! There are an increasing number of uses in the real world for this form: from electrical apparatus (within TV and computer display screens and high energy particle accelerators); to city-wide communications networks (the so-called Manhattan Street

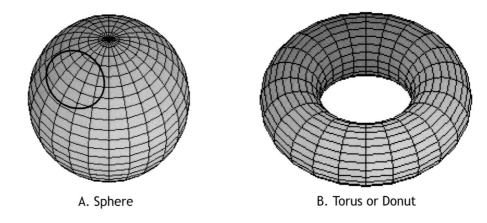

A. Sphere   B. Torus or Donut

Figure 7.2 Closed surfaces with differing topologies

Figure 7.3 GCHQ Building, South West England

Network system); and high-tech buildings such as the Athens 2004 Olympic stadium and the new headquarters for the UK Intelligence gathering services (GCHQ, Figure 7.3).

Returning to our starting point, that of dimension, we can see that it is closely related to our intuitive ideas about number and counting, but on closer inspection it is more complex. An interesting example is to compare producing a map of the countries of the world on a sheet of paper or a sphere, versus the same exercise on a torus. In the first two cases we can colour the map with only 4 separate colours, which is a remarkable result that was originally proposed in the 1850s and only proved to be correct in 1976 (and then by rather unusual means involving the use of some 10,000 computer generated diagrams). A minimum of 7 colours is required for a similar coloured map on a one-fold torus. Although both cases are clearly 2 dimensional surfaces, the differences in their connectivity are highly significant.

7.4 Dimensional analysis

In the preceding sub-sections we have seen that dimensions may have Integer or non-Integer values, depending on the kind of objects we are looking at and how we decide to define dimension. When examining many practical problems and equations it is often useful to check that the dimensions included in the expressions match your expectations. For example, if you are told that the equation for the *surface* area of a sphere of radius, r, is $S=4\pi r^3/3$, you might become immediately suspicious because it involves a term r^3, which implies that it is 3 dimensional whereas a surface is a 2 dimensional object. The formula is actually that for the volume of a sphere. This kind of simple dimensionality checking is an example of *dimensional analysis*, and rather like our previous analysis of magnitude, provides a quick way of ensuring that an expression makes broad sense. We have actually used this form of analysis in a small way already when we looked at the equations for the time a pendulum takes to swing to and fro (its period), and the computation of the universal gravitational constant, G. In these, and similar expressions, the term dimension is extended to include not just spatial dimensions, but all of the units involved, such as those involving time (T) or mass (M).

Dimensional analysis can take us further than simply checking our equations. We can derive new expressions by examining the dimensionality of certain problems. For example, earlier when looking at gravity I quoted the formula derived by Huygens for the (semi-) period, t, of a simple pendulum in terms of its length, l:

$$t = \pi \sqrt{(l/g)}$$

But where did this formula come from? One way of obtaining its overall form is through dimensional analysis. In this paragraph I use an approach based on that given by Körner (1996). The key idea is to try and find a relationship between all the variables involved which is dimensionless, i.e. does not change in size when we change the *units* involved (such as yards or metres for length, seconds or hours for time, and kilograms or pounds for mass). The main variables in an idealised simple pendulum are: the length of the pendulum, l; the mass, m, of the pendulum bob (the bit at the end); the time taken to swing from one side to the other and back again, t; and the gravitational force, g, acting upon the bob. With the exception of g, all the other variables m, l and t are already in their basic dimensional units (dimensionality of 1) say M, L and T, but we know that gravitational force is an acceleration, i.e. of the form g=length/time^2 or of the form L/T^2. So to produce a dimensionless variable, x say, we must set $x=gt^2/l$ (using t^2/l to cancel out the effect of L/T^2). Now observations of real-world pendulums have shown that for any given m and l, the (semi-) period of swing is a constant, say A, so A=gt$^2/l$, and therefore $t=\sqrt{(Al/g)}$ or $t=C\sqrt{(l/g)}$ where C is some constant — which turns out to be π, the result produced by Huygens (using different means) back in the mid 16th century.

Notice that the mass, m, did not enter the equation, confirming that the time taken for a pendulum swing is independent of the size (mass) of the bob used (as Galileo had originally suggested). It also shows that to double the period of a pendulum its length must be increased by a factor of 4 and to halve it, the length is reduced to a quarter. Since a one second pendulum, as used in long case (grandfather) clocks, is just under 1 metre, this means that a clock designed for a mantelpiece or shelf can have a pendulum of only 25cms (around 10 inches) as long as it ticks twice as fast, and a 2 second pendulum needs to be 4 metres, or around 13 feet long, which is far from practical. In fact such clocks have been made in the past — two clocks with 2-second pendulums were designed by Thomas Tompion in 1676 and installed in the old Greenwich Observatory in London (n.b. for clocks the period is usually described for one swing rather than a to-and-fro swing).

8 KISSING NUMBERS AND CANNONBALLS

I shall conclude this part of the book with a discussion of an interesting, but slightly obscure problem, that of kissing numbers. These numbers have nothing to do with personal or cultural propensities for kissing. However, they have a lot to do with cannonballs, balloons, snooker, molecular models, packing problems and lattices.

The original question relating to kissing numbers was reputedly posed by Sir Walter Raleigh in 1606. He was interested in finding how many cannonballs were in a stack of a given size, and how much space on deck such a stack would occupy. An example arrangement in the form of a pyramid is shown in the photograph below.

The number of cannonballs in a typical stack with a square, rectangular or triangular base is fairly simple to calculate. For example, with a square base made up of 6 cannonballs on each side there will be 6x6 in the lowest layer, 5x5 in the next layer and so on, summing the squares, until there is just one cannonball at the top, so 36+25+16+9+4+1=91 in total. The general formula for the number of cannonballs with square base n is: $S=n(n+1)(2n+1)/6$; and for a triangular base is very similar: $T=n(n+1)(n+2)/6$. Both formulas can be obtained using Maple's sum() function, for example for the square case:

Figure 8.1 Kissing Numbers and Cannonballs (Stack of cannonballs, Rye, East Sussex, UK)

```
z:=sum('k^2','k'=1..n): ' this line calculates the sum as an expression in terms of n
factor(z); ' this line arranges the resulting sum in the same form as S, above
```

However, the best way to arrange the projectiles is less obvious. This question was studied and generalised by the astronomer Johannes Kepler (1571-1630) who asked "What is the densest possible packing of spheres in space?". The simple answer is immediately apparent to most people who have seen a display of round fruit stacked neatly on a market stall — an arrangement in which layers of fruit just touch each other (*kissing*, Figure 8.2A) with additional layers offset so the fruit nestles neatly into the dimples provided by the layer below (Figure 8.2B). Each layer is like a large number of snooker or pool balls tightly packed together, with every ball just touching 6 of its neighbours. But the second layer, which is offset from the first, kisses three spheres below it and three above, so the kissing number for spheres of the same size in 3D is at least 12. Interestingly enough this is not a proof that the answer is 12, just that it must be at least 12.

The standard compact layered 3D hexagonal arrangement is known as 'hexagon closest packing', or HCP, as shown in Figure 8.2B, HCP position. This indicates where the third layer of spheres is to be placed. Many metals, such as Magnesium, Zinc and Titanium have an HCP molecular structure. There is another hexagon-based arrangement, known as 'cubic close packing', or CCP. This variant is obtained when the third layer of the hexagonal stack is arranged so that the spheres are not located directly above the first layer, but in dimples above the holes in layer 1 (Figure 8.2B, CCP position). This is tricky to visualise, so is worth checking it is true using a stack of fruit, golf balls or footballs — whatever you have to hand. The molecular structure of a large number of metals

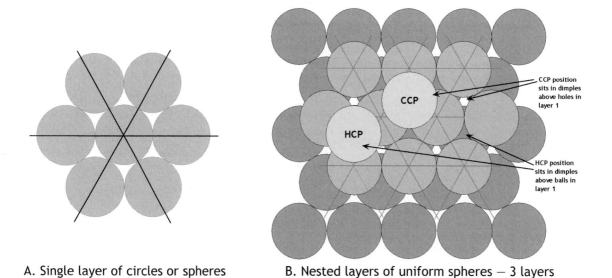

A. Single layer of circles or spheres   B. Nested layers of uniform spheres — 3 layers

Figure 8.2 Circle and sphere packing

follows the CCP pattern rather than HCP, including Calcium, Copper, Aluminium, Silver and Gold.

There remains the possibility that if you have a single sphere suspended in space, you might be able to pack more than 12 spheres around it (see the computer-generated image on the inside front cover of this book). This open-space pattern is similar to the arrangement of the balloons in Larry Walter's epic flight, although in his case the balloons would not have been entirely rigid or perfectly spherical, and the tether lines would have affected the arrangement of the 40+ weather balloons. In 1874 a proof was provided that there was not enough room for a 13th sphere, but this proof turned out to be incomplete. And later it was shown that there are an unlimited number of ways of arranging the 12 surrounding spheres such that each kisses the single central sphere, in most cases without all the surrounding spheres touching each other. These findings made it very probable that the kissing number in 3D was indeed 12, but highlighted the complexity of the problem. Finally, in 1998, an exhaustive (computational) proof was provided by Professor Tom Hales from the University of Pittsburg that 12 is indeed the maximum number possible and is also the densest possible packing of spheres in 3D. With this arrangement 74% (or the fraction $\pi/\sqrt{18}$ to be precise) of the available space is occupied.

You will have noticed in Figure 8.2 that each layer generates a horizontal lattice of triangular (or hexagonal) form through the centres of the circles. In 3D additional lines may be drawn between the centres of the spheres in different layers, extending the triangular plane lattice to a variety of 3D lattices. There is a great deal of interest in such lattices, for many reasons. Some of this is largely academic — for example, trying to determine the kissing numbers for higher dimensions (it is 24 for 4 dimensions... or maybe 25!) — but much research has more practical objectives. Some of these include: discovering improved methods for searching large datasets; developing new ways of systematically analysing complex problems for a 'best' combination of values (optimisation problems); understanding crystal structures and their formation; and designing engineering structures, such as bridges, domes and glass-hung buildings.

With a square lattice in 2D the kissing number is clearly 4, and interestingly enough in 3D it is 12, the same as with HCP. This is because the dimples in each layer are made up from 4 spheres so each sphere in the layer above touches 4 spheres below and 4 above, giving 12 in total. In fact this arrangement is actually the same as HCP, although this is not obvious at first sight. It has its own name: *face-centred cubic* packing, or FCC. Obviously if the spheres in the different layers were directly above one another, i.e. not nestling into the dimples, the kissing numbers would be smaller — 6 for a square or cubic lattice packing and 8 for a triangular or hexagonal lattice packing.

If you try to pack footballs into a cubic box the number you can include will depend on the size (edge length, s) of the box relative to the radius, r, of the football. With $r=1$ (i.e. diameter=2) and $s=2$ a single football will just fit in the box. With two footballs the smallest box has sides $s=2+2/\sqrt{3}$ (i.e. $s=3.154...$) and the balls must be packed slightly offset, e.g. bottom left corner and top right corner. Some of the 'best' packings are with 8 footballs, where the balls are arranged in a square lattice arrangement (with 4 footballs directly above 4, and s=4) and 14 foot-balls, where the balls are arranged in an HCP-like format (5 above 4 above 5, and s=4.828...). Surprisingly, similar issues arise if you were packing cubic objects in cubic boxes. With 9 or 10 unit cubes there is a problem, because you cannot fit them neatly into a larger cube (it is easy with 1 or 8 of course). In this case the smallest box they can fit in has sides s=2.707... (discovered by E Friedman in 1998). The arrangement consists of two layers of 4 cubes tucked into the box corners, with the remaining 1 or 2 cubes squeezed in between them at 45 degrees. Curiously, it has been shown that the most compact form of packing for balls in boxes (in terms of box space used) is a long rectangular box, ignoring the inconvenience of having a very long thin box. But this is provided there are less than 50 balls to pack. After that it gets a bit complicated and with 56 or more balls it is definitely better to pack them into a box that is not a long tube.

A related question, of perhaps greater interest, involves removing the constraint that all the objects are the same size and shape. If we start by removing the uniform size constraint, but limit our consideration to circles and spheres, the problem and solutions expand considerably. For example, with circles of mixed sizes an endless variety of planar packing arrangements are possible (Figure 8.3). There are a surprising range of applications for mixed size circle and sphere packings, including: physical packaging design (perhaps unexpectedly, one of the world's largest industries); molecular modelling (common salt, for example, which is a mixture of larger chloride ions and smaller sodium ions); mapping the human brain; artistic design (art, textiles, physical tiles); multi-thread cable design; virology and many other areas of research.

If the final constraint is removed, that of shape, the range of possibilities and applications expands

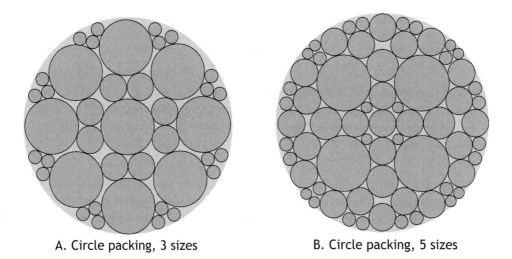

A. Circle packing, 3 sizes   B. Circle packing, 5 sizes

Figure 8.3 Variable size circle packing (circular boundary)

still further. In 2D the densest possible regular packing consists of hexagonal tiles (i.e. the triangular or hexagonal lattice). In the case of the hexagonal lattice the edge length is minimised, thus requiring the minimum possible amount of material per enclosed unit area for its construction. This is a key factor explaining why bees and wasps produce hexagonal rather than square honeycombs — they require the least amount of material. The 3D equivalent of the 2D hexagonal lattice is called a regular rhombic dodecahedron (a 12 sided object) — quite a mouthful! It provides a compact but somewhat odd-shaped 3D packaging arrangement with no gaps. The semi-precious crystal garnet grows in this form as do the seeds of the pomegranate (approximately) and ball bearings when carefully compressed until all the gaps have been squashed out.

Much more complex 2D and 3D compact packing shapes have been developed, not least in art, where the Dutch woodcut specialist Maurits Escher devised many of the best known images of the 20th century from complex interlocking (tessellating) forms. He had a particular interest in representing mathematical forms and ideas, one of which (representing infinite space) is shown in Figure 8.4. This model of the universe can be seen as 'hot' near the centre and cooling towards

Figure 8.4 Circle Limit III, M Escher

the extremities. In the hotter areas everything is large — your own size, the length of your steps and the length of all measuring equipment. As you walk towards the cooler extremities you, and all other things shrink to the same extent. Because absolutely everything shrinks you cannot detect that your size is changing, and your steps are getting smaller and smaller. This gives you the impression of an infinite universe although from outside, in another universe, we are able to observe that this space is really finite.

PART II: EXPERIMENTATION AND COMPUTATIONAL METHODS

"Now that the computer has given new power to the eye and geometry, their usefulness in science and mathematics has been revived and should again be recognised. Blind analytic manipulation is never enough. Formalism, however effective in the short run, is never enough." Beniot Mandelbrot, 2002

In Part I of this book I provided details of many of the building blocks needed in order to understand the terminology and some of the methods commonly used by scientists and mathematicians. In this second Part of the book I explore a wide range of ideas and procedures using largely numerical methods applied to practical problems, often calculated with the assistance of various modern software tools. This approach is very powerful, since it shows the actual values associated with a process, and attempts to use these to identify broader principles. However, there are some important notes of caution that I must add before commencing:

- The first is that numerical results, or *outputs*, reflect the *inputs* — in this case the models and procedures we decide to use and the initial values selected. If any of these inputs are inappropriate or incorrect, the outputs certainly will be misleading or simply wrong

- The second issue is that numerical procedures may be subject to errors and/or lack of convergence, which may or may not be observable for the range of data we are examining. There is an entire discipline called Numerical Analysis that seeks to understand and then minimise or avoid such issues. You will already be familiar with some of these issues from the discussions on precision and accuracy in Part I

- A third issue is that numerical methods are not an alternative to devising and using equations and applying logic to complex problems — they simply provide a valuable set of experimental methods within a much broader collection of analytical tools

- Finally, it is important to be aware that there are many problems that are very sensitive to the input values, so require extra care and experimentation. For example, suppose you have a search procedure that involves finding some buried treasure having been given a map and instructions. You are told that the procedure is: find the big tree shown on your map and then take one hundred steps due South, 30 steps due East and start digging. In this instance you only need a very slight deviation from due South at the beginning, say 1 degree, and you will miss the target by around 6 metres (this ignores what we mean by a 'step'). Some examples of such sensitivities are given in the Section covering Population Modelling and related procedures (Section 13). It may also be the case that the most interesting or important data or results occur at extreme points, or around critical values of the inputs, so examination of such sensitivities is typically an essential part of analysis.

9 CREDIT CARD AND EMAIL SECURITY

Credit card details, e-commerce transactions and 'secure' emails use a variety of encryption methods to achieve a level of security that is deemed commercially satisfactory (the word encrypt comes from the Greek kryptos, meaning hidden). This is not as secure as military authorities require, and the US Government requires commercial organisations to use encryption levels and techniques that it can decode, but hopefully others cannot! In many cases the encryption is based on the use of large prime numbers, coupled with the observation we made in Part I that multiplication is a lot easier than division or factoring. In this case, multiplying two large prime numbers together gives a very large number that can be extremely difficult to separate into its two factors, unless of course you know one of them already. We can use these observations to encrypt a credit card number, such as:

5414 5678 1234 9876

I will show that using two randomly selected large prime numbers (30 decimal digit numbers, or roughly 100 binary digits), this card number can be encrypted using key values that are public (i.e. non secret) as:

1442587200969413151307110822991688184162198601592059759683694

and that decrypting this without the private or secret key is extremely difficult. I also show that this procedure can be extended easily to handle text messages, such as "this message is secret!".

First of all we will describe the steps involved in generating an encrypted message, using a procedure devised in 1977 by three US mathematicians. This system is known as RSA after the authors' initials: Rivest, Shamir and Adelman. It enables a user to publish the keys for encrypting a message you may want to send to them, but these keys are of little or no use to you or anyone else in attempting to decipher the message once encrypted. Only the user can perform the decryption using another, secret key. Having described the method and tried it with a very simple example, I will then show how it can be applied to our credit card number. For full details on exactly why this procedure works see Meyer and Matyas (1982) or Schneier (1996), or one of the many descriptions available on the web.

9.1 The RSA procedure

The user takes two large primes, p and q, and calculates their product $n=pq$. He or she then chooses a number, e, less than n that has no common factors with $r=(p-1)(q-1)$. The public key is the pair n and e. For example, with $p=5$ and $q=11$ we have $n=55$ and $r=4*10=40$. If we choose $e=7$, say, we can see it is less than *n* and 7 does not divide into 40, so it has no common factors with *r*. Another number, *d*, is then found, subject to the condition that (*e**d-1) is divisible by the least common multiple (LCM) of (*p*-1) and (*q*-1), which we will call *t*. Using the same numbers as above, we seek a value d such that 7*d-1 can be divided by the LCM of 4 and 10, which is 20 (see next paragraph for more details). So if *d*=3, say, we have 7*3-1=20 which is OK. The *private key* is the pair *n* and *d*.

To explain what the LCM is, let's use *p*=5 and *q*=11 again. Then (*p*-1)=4 and (*q*-1)=10, and the smallest number that is a multiple of both of these values is 20 (4*5=20 and 10*2=20) — this is the LCM. If you need to compute this and working it out by hand is inconvenient, Maple has this operation provided by its built-in function lcm(). The factors of *n* (i.e. *p* and *q*) can either be kept secret or destroyed. If *p* and *q* are large enough it is virtually impossible to obtain the private key, *d*, from the public key (*n* and *e*).

Encryption and decryption of a message, *m*, proceeds as follows:

1. The receiver (our original user), R, distributes his or her public key pair (*e*,*n*)
2. The sender, S, composes a message, *m*, and then uses R's public key to encrypt the message and form the encrypted text, *c*, using the expression: $c=m^e$(mod *n*)
3. S sends the encrypted text *c*, to R.
4. R, decrypts *c* and retrieves the original message, *m*, using: $m=c^d$(mod *n*)

Let us test this procedure using very small primes initially, so we can do the sums by hand. We start with the values for *p* and *q* we used a little earlier:

Let *p*=5, *q*=11, *n*=*pq*=55, so *r*=(*p*-1)(*q*-1)=40 and *t*=LCM(4,10)=20. We now need to choose *e*, such that *e*<*n* (55) and *e* has no common factors with *r*, so any multiple of 2 or 5 are not acceptable (because *r*=40=2^3*5). We could choose any number less than 55, but it is simplest to choose a prime such as 7, 11 or 13..., so let's choose *e*=7, as before. We now need to find the private key, *d*, using the condition *e**d-1(mod *t*)≡0. If d=3 we find 7*3-1=20(mod 20)≡0, which is fine; *d*=23 would have worked also, but I want to stick with small numbers for the present. Now we are ready to encrypt a message using the public key pair (7,55), and then check to see that we can decrypt it using the private key pair (3,55).

Let the message be *m*=2, so to encrypt it we carry out the four steps:

1. Encryption: $c=m^e$(mod *n*)=2^7(mod 55)≡18 (because 128/55=2+18/55, so we just keep the remainder, 18)
2. S sends the number 18 to R, and then
3. R needs to decrypt it using the private key pair (3,55)
4. R calculates c^d(mod *n*)=18^3(mod 55)≡2 because 18^3=5832=106*55+2 so R reads the original message, *m*=2; success!

This example used very small primes and as a result is not at all difficult to factor *n*=55 to retrieve the original primes, 5 and 11, and thus obtain the private key, *d*=3. In 1997 a detailed evaluation assessment of the security of 512-bit RSA keys showed that the factors could be obtained with a few months of effort, and computer power and techniques have moved on a great deal since then. For this reason current recommendations are for key sizes of at least 768 bits for personal use, 1024 bits for corporate use, and 2048 bits for extremely valuable keys. Security can be increased by changing a user's keys regularly (e.g. every year or more frequently if necessary). If you look in the "Help, About" menu of your favourite web browser it should tell you the cipher strength included within the browser for handling security — mine shows 128bit at present, which speaks volumes.

We now return to our credit card encryption problem, which involves securely encrypting a 16 decimal digit number. To achieve this we first need some large primes, and we will start by using the Maple software tools to help us. Using Maple we can examine whether a given number is a prime or not, and if not, what its factors are. For example, taking the number 8512, we can check to see if it is prime or not by asking Maple to find its factors, as follows (Maple's results are shown in bold, and the symbol := is Maple's standard *assignment* statement rather than equality):

```
x:=8512;
ifactor(x); (2⁶)(7)(19)
```

Because 8512 can be factorised it is not a prime number (which we already know, since it is even). But we can find out what the next prime number is after 8512, as follows:

```
nextprime(x); 8513
isprime(8513); true
```

So we see that the very next Integer, 8513, is prime, but this time we have used another feature in Maple to determine this. The reason that isprime() is provided as a built-in function is to enable checks on large prime numbers to be carried out quickly. It is much quicker to use this function than trying to factorise a large prime — by large we mean a prime number with a large number of digits, and we can use nextprime() to obtain some for use in our credit card encryption model. Maple includes a range of other functions that are useful when working with primes, including ithprime(k) which will return the value of the prime that is k^{th} in sequence (where you specify k).

Here is the start of the example which we will be using — the initial large primes, *p* and *q*, are created by generating a large random number using Maple's rand() function and then asking for the nextprime() after this value:

```
r1:=rand(10^30)():
p:=nextprime(r1); 307198155590763466429392673741
```

```
r2:=rand(10^30)():
q:=nextprime(r2); 510973272600608981219760099401
n:=p*q; 156970046899083472681446727266882536036450128450383322529141
r:=(p-1)*(q-1); 156970046899083472681446727266064364608258756002734169756000
isprime(n); false
length(n); 60
```

So *n* is not a prime, and we know that *p* and *q* are its factors, but if we try and use the ifactor() function to find these factors it will probably fail because it takes too long — with larger primes the problem of finding the factors becomes almost impossible. We now need to obtain a public encryption exponent *e*, and from this, the private decryption exponent, *d*.

To obtain *e* we must have *e*<*n* and *e* relatively prime to *r*. For now we will keep it simple and choose *e* as another prime, much smaller than *n*, and check to see if the biggest number that will divide into both *e* and *r* is 1, if so then the value we have chosen for e is relatively prime to *r*. The process for checking for the biggest divisor is called finding the greatest common divisor, and the function gcd() in Maple will do this for us:

```
r3:=rand(10^10)():
e:=nextprime(r3); 5473509491
gcd(e,r); 1
```

So *r* is not divisible by *e*. Finally, we need *d*, the private (decryption) exponent. We know that the condition that we must satisfy is *e**d-1(mod *r*)≡0. Although we shall not justify it here, we can rearrange this expression just like an ordinary equation, so we rearrange it to give us *e**d(mod *r*)≡1 and again to give *d*=1/*e* (mod *r*). Maple enables us to do this directly:

```
d := eval(1/e mod r);
62617864344037113772632706130221320884644766412055635027611
```

So now we have all the elements to enable us to encrypt our credit card number. The numbers e, n and d are large, but this is not a problem since the expressions involved can be computed very rapidly. For ease of use we will define two functions, one called encrypt and the other decrypt, and use these on the 16 digits of our card number. As per our earlier discussion on modular arithmetic in Part I, the function Power() which is specifically designed for use with modular arithmetic should be used rather than a^e in this case, otherwise an overflow error will be reported (the symbol -> shown here is Maple's assignment statement for functions):

```
encrypt:=(m,e,n) -> Power(m,e) mod n:
decrypt:=(m,d,n) -> Power(m,d) mod n:
card:=5414567812349876:
```

t	116		a	97
h	104			32
i	105		s	115
s	115		e	101
	32		c	99
i	105		r	114
s	115		e	101
	32		t	116
			!	33

Figure 9.1 ASCII encoding of test message

m1:=encrypt(card,e,n);
144258720096941315130711082299168818416219860159205975683694
m2:=decrypt(m1,d,n); **5414 5678 1234 9876**

So we have successfully encrypted and decrypted a 16-digit card number using this procedure. Note that each time we restart the process described we will generate a different set of values for *p* and *q*, so if we wish to use a particular pair for a series of transactions or for some time (e.g. a year) we must omit the randomised generation step in subsequent usage.

What about our text message, "this is a secret!". In this case we can change the text into a numeric string using the ASCII codes for each character, and then encrypt it in the same way in blocks or all in one go. The coding is shown in Figure 9.1 (created using the Excel code() function). The numeric sequence 1161041051153210511532 is the encoding of the first section of this message ('this is'), and if we plug this into our encrypt() function it will happily produce a new magic number that we can safely transmit to the intended recipient, who will decrypt it and convert it back from ASCII codes into the original text string.

Real-world encryption systems are of course, more sophisticated than this, but in many cases build on these ideas to provide very secure and effectively unbreakable message security — your credit card transactions and encrypted messages *should* be commercially safe, at least for the time being!

9.2   PGP

One of the most widely used developments of procedures such as RSA is the so-called "Pretty Good Privacy" or PGP procedure. This is a hybrid of conventional cryptographic techniques and RSA-like methods. PGP is much faster than RSA for longer messages and has additional security features, such as pre-compression of the message (makes the source less obvious and more compact for transmission) and creation of the encrypted message using a randomly generated encryption key that only applies for the current session. The decryption key is then encrypted using the recipient's public key and included with the PGP message so the recipient can decrypt the whole message.

For more details, see the International PGP home page: http://www.pgpi.org or similar information available from the many PGP web sites.

10 DIGITAL IMAGE PROCESSING

Digital photography and digital images have recently become the norm rather than the exception. We have become familiar with clips of computer screens ("screen shots"), digital cameras and video, medical imaging systems, mobile phones that provide picture messaging and satellite images that depict the weather or images of landuse. In each of these examples the images are represented as a series of points known as 'picture elements' or *pixels* in two dimensions. This data forms a large array, perhaps 1000x1000 elements or more, each of which may have an associated numerical code indicating its greyscale or colour value, as described in Part I. If the latter is coded in 256 levels, or 8 bits, the image size (uncompressed) would be 8 million bits, or just under a Megabyte. In practice there is a great deal of information in most digital images that is repetitive, and a variety of coding and compression schemes are used as standard. Examples include: the widely used compressed Image Formats GIF and TIF (compressed versions); the Joint Photographic Experts Group formats, or JPEG formats; and the Motion Picture Experts Group formats, or MPEG formats (which includes the popular MPEG-3 or MP3 audio file encoding system). In the following two Sections we will investigate manipulation of the geometry of a picture in its original, uncompressed form.

10.1   Image rotation

Most digital cameras take pictures that are *landscape* in format. That is, the width of the picture is greater than its height. When taking a close-up portrait it is often better to turn the camera through 90° and take advantage of this to obtain a good head-and-shoulders picture. When you load the images onto your computer this picture will be incorrectly oriented for viewing and printing, so you will probably wish to rotate it back through 90° again. A similar problem arises when you take a picture with the camera slightly at an angle to the subject, and you then wish to straighten it out or *rectify* it. This is common problem with aerial photography for a number of reasons, including the difficulty of ensuring that the plane and bearing of flight is constant and 'level'. We shall examine how basic rectification may be achieved through image rotation using simple matrix operations.

We start with a single picture element or *pixel*, as a point A with coordinates $(x,y)=(3,4)$ as shown in Figure 10.1. For the moment we will ignore pixel colour, and assume the image is binary (i.e. black and white or similar). We want to rotate this point through 90° around the origin (0,0) so that it ends up at point B, with coordinates (x',y'), which are to be determined. In fact from the diagram we can see that $x'=-4$ and $y'=3$.

The point A can be represented as a column vector $p=[3,4]^T$ (the superscript T here means

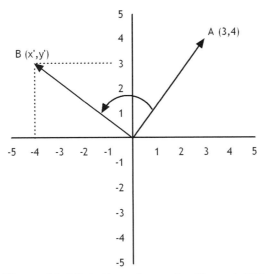

Figure 10.1 Rotation of a vector through 90°

transform, as we saw in Part I). We want to end up with a vector *q*=[-4,3]^T, which is the point B. We can achieve this by pre-multiplying *p* by a very simple 2x2 matrix, **R**, such that *q*=**R***p. The details are shown below:

$$\begin{bmatrix} x' \\ y' \end{bmatrix} = \begin{bmatrix} 0 & -1 \\ 1 & 0 \end{bmatrix} * \begin{bmatrix} 3 \\ 4 \end{bmatrix} = \begin{bmatrix} -4 \\ 3 \end{bmatrix}$$

In this case the entries in **R** are 0 on the principal diagonal and -1 and 1 on the opposite diagonal. This procedure has the desired result, although we have yet to see why it works and whether it can be generalised. For this we need to investigate a little more.

In principle this process could be carried out for every pixel in the original picture, with the result that a complete set of newly aligned (rotated) pixels would be created, showing your photo in the orientation you require (but moved across to the left in this example). Alternatively, many or possibly all pixels could be adjusted at once. This time, let us take several pixels and rotate them all at once. In this case we have a set of 5 points, as shown in black in Figure 10.2

The rotation equation is simply:

$$\begin{bmatrix} \mathbf{x'} \\ \mathbf{y'} \end{bmatrix} = \begin{bmatrix} 0 & -1 \\ 1 & 0 \end{bmatrix} * \begin{bmatrix} 3 & 2 & 1 & 2 & 3 \\ 4 & 3 & 2 & 1 & 0 \end{bmatrix} = \begin{bmatrix} -4 & -3 & -2 & -1 & 0 \\ 3 & 2 & 1 & 2 & 3 \end{bmatrix}$$

so is very similar to the previous example. In this case the column vector on the left hand side represents a set of five point pairs, (**x'**,**y'**), so I have shown them here in bold type. In fact, we see that a pattern has emerged, enabling this kind of rotation to be completed without

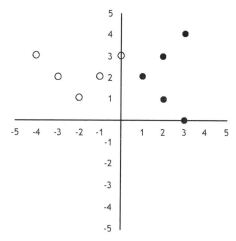

Figure 10.2 Image pixel rotation through 90°

matrix multiplication, since all it involves is swapping the two rows and changing the sign of the resultant first row. Rotating through other multiples of 90° forwards or backwards (clockwise or anticlockwise) result in similar patterns that can be exploited for very rapid image manipulation.

We now need to generalise this operation to handle two further conditions:

(i) rotation by an arbitrary angle, θ, in the range [-2π,2π]; and
(ii) positioning the rotated image in a convenient place, for example with its centre matching the centre of the original set of pixels.

The first part of this is simple. We make the observation (guessing, or using prior knowledge based on the geometry involved) that the matrix **R** is actually of the form:

$$\mathbf{R} = \begin{bmatrix} \cos(\theta) & -\sin(\theta) \\ \sin(\theta) & \cos(\theta) \end{bmatrix}$$

If we put θ=π/2 into this matrix we get the pattern of 0s and 1s we have just been using. However, suppose we have θ=π/4, i.e. only a 45° rotation. From our earlier work on cos() and sin() we know that they are both 1/√2=0.7071... for θ=π/4, so we can put these values into the matrix equation and see what happens:

$$\begin{bmatrix} x' \\ y' \end{bmatrix} = \begin{bmatrix} 0.7071 & -0.7071 \\ 0.7071 & 0.7071 \end{bmatrix} * \begin{bmatrix} 3 & 2 & 1 & 2 & 3 \\ 4 & 3 & 2 & 1 & 0 \end{bmatrix} = \begin{bmatrix} -0.7071 & -0.7071 & -0.7071 & 0.7071 & 2.1213 \\ 4.9497 & 3.5355 & 2.1213 & 2.1213 & 2.1213 \end{bmatrix}$$

This result gives the image shown in Figure 10.3 when plotted. As can be seen the rotation is 45°, as desired.

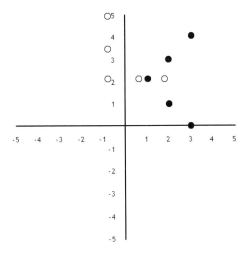

Figure 10.3 Image pixel rotation through 45°

This just leaves the positioning of the image, which we may prefer to be based on the original set of points. In this case we need to move, or *translate*, the new set of points, back to the midpoint of the original set, (x_0,y_0). To achieve this, the rotated set would need to be moved down and to the right, perhaps by a fixed adjustment to the coordinates of each point. The value that we might choose could be determined by the difference in the average values of the two sets of data, before and after, *p* and *q*. In our example for *p* we have (x_0,y_0)=(2.2,2) and for *q* (x'_0,y'_0)= (0.1414,2.9698), so the difference is roughly (2,-1), and the final result is shown in Figure 10.4 by the set of grey dots on our diagram, now including translation as well as rotation.

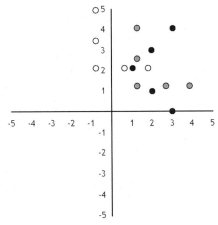

Figure 10.4 Rotation and translation of an image

A more convenient way to carry out this kind of operation in matrix form is:

$$\begin{bmatrix} x' \\ y' \end{bmatrix} = \begin{bmatrix} \cos(\theta) & -\sin(\theta) \\ \sin(\theta) & \cos(\theta) \end{bmatrix} * \begin{bmatrix} (x - x_0) \\ (y - y_0) \end{bmatrix} + \begin{bmatrix} x_0 \\ y_0 \end{bmatrix}$$

where the $(x-x_0)$ and $(y-y_0)$ expressions apply to each point, for example the point (3,4) becomes (3-2.2, 4-2)=(0.8,2). So writing this out in full we have:

$$\begin{bmatrix} x' \\ y' \end{bmatrix} = \begin{bmatrix} 0.7071 & -0.7071 \\ 0.7071 & 0.7071 \end{bmatrix} * \begin{bmatrix} 0.8 & -0.2 & -1.2 & -0.2 & 0.8 \\ 2 & 1 & 0 & -1 & -2 \end{bmatrix} + \begin{bmatrix} 2.2 \\ 2 \end{bmatrix} = \begin{bmatrix} 1.3515 & 1.3515 & 1.3515 & 2.7657 & 4.1799 \\ 3.9799 & 2.5657 & 1.1515 & 1.1515 & 1.1515 \end{bmatrix}$$

If you add up the numbers in the first row and divide by 5 you get 2.2, and for the second row, 2, so the resulting image has the same central point as the original image.

You may have spotted one or two problems with these ideas, or found difficulties if you have tried to implement the procedure with a real digital image. One problem is that if we rotate an image of say 100x100 pixels through 45°, it may require a larger matrix of pixels to display and store it. For example, the image illustrated in Figure 10.5 with a 45° rotation occupies a much larger frame than the original. One solution to this problem is to retain the original image, and apply the rotation as and when we wish to view or print it. But this processing takes time, and may be only one of several changes we wish to make to the original image. Another approach is to store the

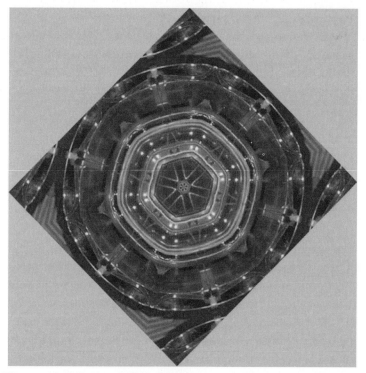

Figure 10.5 Rotated digital image — nominal storage increase

new, much larger image, but compress the large amount of 'white' space so that it does not impact storage too much — in the example shown, the image when rotated is roughly double the size of the original, but only occupies 10% more space on disk.

A second problem is that the final values in the output matrix are not Integers, but a picture image is stored as a set of rows and columns that have Integer positions. If we apply simple rounding rules we find that the output picture will contain lots of holes (black pixels) where no pixel in the source image has been translated into the destination image. There are various solutions to this problem, but the most effective is to reverse the process and start with the output image, for which we already have Integer pixels. Then use a modified form of our rotation matrix, now with negative rotation, by an angle of -θ, to identify the pixels in the source image:

$$\begin{bmatrix} x \\ y \end{bmatrix} = \begin{bmatrix} \cos(-\theta) & -\sin(-\theta) \\ \sin(-\theta) & \cos(-\theta) \end{bmatrix} * \begin{bmatrix} (x'-x_0) \\ (y'-y_0) \end{bmatrix} + \begin{bmatrix} x_0 \\ y_0 \end{bmatrix}$$

10.2 Image adjustment

There are many ways in which an image may be altered, in addition to the simple processes of rotation and translation. For example, flipping an image horizontally or vertically, which can be achieved by copying the rows or columns of the image matrix into a secondary matrix in reverse order (i.e. from last to first).

Resizing images is more complex than rotation and translation, since this may be achieved in many different ways. For example, if an image is to be reduced in size by half in both directions, one method is to throw away every second row and column. The result is an image whose quality is reduced and cannot be recovered unless a copy of the original has been retained (on disk or in memory). Better approaches exist. The same idea could be applied to doubling an image in size, by including each row and column twice, but again far better approaches exist. Other examples of common adjustments include changing the colour or contrast, sharpening or blurring an image, trimming and resizing, and automatic pattern recognition (e.g. car licence plate reading). Many of these processes are known as *filtering*, since they involve applying some form of *filter* to every pixel of the image.

One alternative when re-sizing (which could include stretching the image by different amounts in each direction) is to generate a new image by *interpolation* of the original image. This involves trying to obtain a good estimate of the value (e.g. colour, intensity) that should be assigned to each pixel of the new image, based on patterns in the original image. Operations of this type often involve applying a small matrix of values (filter or *kernel*) to sections of the original image, pixel-by-pixel, scanning the image from top left to bottom right (sometimes more than once), until the process has been completed.

If a picture is not as sharp or well defined as you would like, you may wish to increase the apparent sharpness. Typically you can achieve this by applying a *filter* or sharpness kernel to every pixel of the source image. A 3x3 kernel matrix is placed over each pixel in the original picture, typically starting one row and column in from the edge, and the values for R, G and B at that point are altered by the values a and b in the kernel matrix. The entries in this kernel matrix should add up to 1, so $a=1$ and $b=9$ is a common choice:

$$\begin{bmatrix} -a & -a & -a \\ -a & +b & -a \\ -a & -a & -a \end{bmatrix}$$

To clarify this, suppose we have the top left hand corner of a picture. We now place the centre of our kernel over the first available position, row 2 column 2 and apply this to each of the R, G and B components of the first block of 9 pixels. For example, suppose in row 1 column 1 the RGB values are [128 0 128] so these become [128-a 0-a 128-a] or [127 0 127] if $a=1$. Note that values adjusted to less than 0 are reset to 0, and values adjusted to over 255 are reset to 255. Once all 9 pixels are adjusted in this way the kernel is moved one position to the right and the process is repeated, now centred on position (2,3). The colour changes resulting from this process may be quite subtle at the individual pixel level, with the pixels at the image edges hardly changing, so you really need to work with a full size image to appreciate the results. We can achieve this by opening a full-size image with any one of the widely available picture editing programs, such as Paint Shop Pro or Adobe Photoshop and using the built-in tools these provide. However, the details of what is going on may be hidden from you and therefore not fully under your own control. With some software packages you may be able to specify your own (i.e. user-defined) filters. An alternative is to write a small computer program or to use image-processing facilities built-in to advanced software tools such as MATLab (Image Processing Toolbox).

Commonly used image filtering operations include:

- **Sharpening** — for which the kernel matrix elements sum to 1 and the matrix is symmetric. Matrix elements are a mix of positive, negative and zero entries.
- **Edge detection** — for which the kernel matrix elements sum to 0 and the matrix is normally symmetric. As with sharpening, matrix elements are a mix of positive, negative and zero entries.
- **Embossing** — for which the kernel matrix elements sum to 0 as per edge detection, but the matrix is asymmetric. It is usual to compute the embossed version of an image on a greyscale version, which is obtained by finding the average value of the R, G and B component as $x=(r+g+b)/3$ for each pixel, and assigning the resulting values in the range [0,255] to a grey scale (where 0=black and 255=white)
- **Blurring** (also known as a *smoothing* or *low-pass* filter, since this reduces or removes extreme values). In this case the kernel matrix elements sum to >1, entries are normally all positive and the matrix is symmetric. Because this process adds values to

every pixel in a progressive manner, reduction of the cumulative effect is often achieved by dividing each kernel value by the sum of its elements, so the final result sums to 1. This latter process is known as *normalisation*

The descriptions here are of typical kernel filters, which are also generally square arrays (e.g. 3x3, 5x5,or 7x7). Examples of each of the three additional kernels (in 3x3 form) are shown below:

Edge detection	$\begin{bmatrix} -1 & -1 & -1 \\ -1 & +8 & -1 \\ -1 & -1 & -1 \end{bmatrix}$	$\begin{bmatrix} -1 & -1 & -1 \\ 0 & 0 & 0 \\ 1 & 1 & 1 \end{bmatrix}$
Embossing	$\begin{bmatrix} 0 & 0 & 0 \\ 0 & 1 & 0 \\ 0 & 0 & -1 \end{bmatrix}$	$\begin{bmatrix} 2 & 0 & 0 \\ 0 & -1 & 0 \\ 0 & 0 & -1 \end{bmatrix}$
Blurring	$\begin{bmatrix} 1 & 2 & 1 \\ 2 & 4 & 2 \\ 1 & 2 & 1 \end{bmatrix}$	$\begin{bmatrix} 1 \\ 2 \\ 1 \end{bmatrix} * \begin{bmatrix} 1 & 2 & 1 \end{bmatrix}$

The last of these examples (blurring) shows that in some cases the kernel can be generated by the multiplication of two vectors, and this enables the computation to be carried out faster because the image can be processed row-wise with the row vector and then column-wise with the column vector. The net result of using vectors is fewer overall calculations. The normalisation (division) factor in this case is 16 (the sum of the kernel matrix elements).

In the illustration below I have applied two of these filters to a photograph of the central section of a lighthouse lens. First I applied an edge detection kernel, in this case using the second version from the set described above. To make the edges visually clearer on output the final image has been inverted (like a photographic negative) by changing each pixel value x to 255-x. In the second of these examples I applied an embossing kernel. In both examples I used a colour image and converted the result to greyscale for illustration here.

Original image

Edge detected version

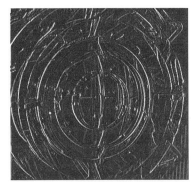

Embossed version

The ideas and matrix and vector algebra used in this Section can be studied in more detail in most basic mathematics texts. Books on digital image processing tend to be more demanding — the classic text on this subject area (updated in 2002 to almost 800 pages) is by Gonzales and Woods. Unless you wish to investigate the subject in detail it is probably best to use pre-built picture processing software and the in-built tools and help files that explain their use.

11 BETTER DIVISION AND MULTIPLICATION

In this example I look at the expressions $x=a/b$ and $x=a*b$, where a and b are Real numbers and b is not equal to 0. The tool I use here, as in many of the examples, is Microsoft's Excel spreadsheet package running on an Intel Pentium 4 processor system under the Windows 2000 operating system. As an initial test case I will look at the rather tricky-looking division problem of finding the value of x, where $x=2987.354/0.08512$.

11.1 Division by progressive subtraction

As I noted in Part I, computers do not apply the traditional procedure of long division to calculate x — they use a range of other approaches. One such method involves progressive subtraction, whilst another involves a mixture of guesswork and iteration. I will examine this second method in a moment, using the computer as an exploratory tool, after first looking at division by subtraction.

A simplified way of looking at progressive subtraction is to recast our division problem as one involving the repeated subtraction of one Integer, b, from another, a, where $a=2987354$ and $b=8512$. This process is followed by multiplication by 100 at the end: $100=10^2$ is used because we multiply the Integer a by 10^{-3} and b by 10^{-5} to obtain the decimal numbers we started with; and finally, because we are dividing by b, we adjust the result by $-3-(-5)=+2$.

If we repeatedly subtract b from a, we find that after 350 subtractions we are left with a remainder of 8154. We could do our multiplication by 100 at this point and continue subtracting to obtain the next 2 digits>0, which would be 95 times with a remainder 6760. So the result is of the form $35095.r$ — the remainder, r, can be determined in the same manner (multiplying the residual by 1000 say, and continuing subtracting to obtain the first few decimal places $.794...$). In practice this example is rather cumbersome and much more efficient algorithms using binary arithmetic make such a procedure very rapid, despite the number of computations required. But another procedure, which is very fast and quite straightforward, is to systematically search for the answer, as we now show.

11.2 Division by iteration

Instead of writing our problem as $x=a/b$ we can write it as $x=a*(1/b)$. In this form we can see that every division of this type is simply a matter of finding the reciprocal, $1/b$, of the divisor b followed by a multiplication. Now, as we saw in the previous example, b can be written in standard (or exponential) form as $c*10^n$, where n is an Integer. For example, if $b=8512$ then

$c=8.512*10^3$, or if $b=0.08512$ then we can write $c=8.512*10^{-3}$. In other words, $x=a*(1/c)*10^n$, where $1 \leq c \leq 10$. So to do a numerical division we can restrict ourselves to finding $y=1/c$, where c lies in the range between 1 and 10, for example $c=8.512$. The exact decimal expression for $1/c$ in this case is 0.1174812030075190, so we can use this answer to check our methods and results.

To do this we are going to use the iterative procedure:

$$y_{i+1}=y_i(2-cy_i)$$

with some starting value y_0. This is sometimes written as:

$$y_{i+1} \rightarrow y_i(2-cy_i)$$

to clarify that it is not really an equation, but a *mapping*. I will continue to use the equation symbol, however, for ease of presentation. So the first iteration equation is:

$$y_1=y_0(2-cy_0)$$

For example, if we use the guess $y_0=0.1$ we find

$$y_1=0.1(2-8.512*0.1)=0.1148$$

which is already quite close to the correct answer (0.11748...). This procedure states that an improved value for $1/c$ can be obtained by a simple sequence of multiplications, assuming that y_0 is a fairly good first guess. The reason for using this iterative form requires knowledge of calculus, and is known as a Newton-Raphson method. For the moment it is sufficient to assume that it is going to work, and try it out. Most computer science books on numerical methods or algorithms describe the background and process in more detail.

If the starting value y_0 is a good guess, i.e. reasonably close to the final answer, this procedure will converge very rapidly. But how should we guess y_0? Well, one thing we can do is experiment — by calculating values for $1/c$ in the range 1-10 and plotting these on a graph, as shown in Figure 11.1. In this case I have created a list of values in Excel from 1 to 10 in steps of 0.2, then a second list giving 1/(these values), and finally asking Excel to plot the result. The smooth-looking curve shows the data, and the two dotted lines show a simple linear approximation to sections of the curve (a piecewise linear approximation).

From this exploration of the values of $1/c$ we can see that a first guess could be 0.1 if c lay between 9 and 10, 0.2 if it lay between 8 and 9, and so forth. Alternatively we could use the linear approximation shown to enable us to guess intermediate results, or a better one that used a linear approximation for every interval of 1 unit (i.e. between 1 and 2, 2 and 3 etc.). Now we

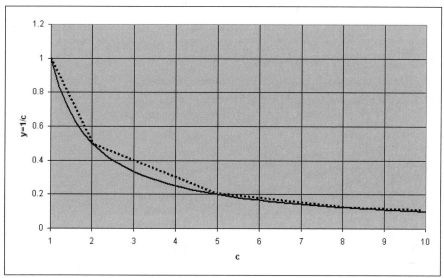

Figure 11.1 Piecewise linear approximation of y=1/c

have c=8.512, and over the interval between 8 and 9 an approximation using a straight line is given by:

y=(1/8+1/9)-(1/8-1/9)*c

Notice that this allows us to get a good first estimate for y_0 by simple multiplications only, because we can pre-calculate 1/8 and 1/9 as decimals with as many digits as we wish. This expression is of the general form y=α_8+β_8*c where α_8 and β_8 are decimal constants that apply for the 8th interval. For each interval a pair of constants apply, and so we could use a look-up table to get these constants, calculate a first approximation to y_0, and then proceed.

If we plug in c=8.512 into this last form of the expression we get y_0=0.117889, so this gives us our guess at the correct answer to 1/8.512. We can now apply our iterative rule:

y_{i+1}=y_i(2-cy_i), and a starting value y_0=0.117889

we then find the values for y_1=0.117889(2-8.512*0.117889)=0.117497..., and by iteration 3 we have 0.117481203... which is precisely the result given by Excel's own division algorithm. The results from Excel are shown in Table 11.1.

If our original guess had been 0.2 it would have taken 7 iterations to reach this result, but any estimate greater than 0.234 would have resulted in divergence, not convergence, so being fairly close to the target is essential! You might like to test these findings with your own numbers, and

Table 11-1 Division by approximation

c	8.512	Difference from 1/c
1/c	0.1174812030075190	
c_0	0.1178890000000000	
c_1	0.1174797874756480	-0.000001415531870788
c_2	0.1174812029904630	-0.000000000017055760
c_3	0.1174812030075190	0.000000000000000000

see what happens with guesses that lie below as well as above those I have described. Now we can determine the value of our original problem, 2987.354/0.08512, by multiplying the result above for c_3 by 2987.354*10², i.e. by 298735.4, giving 35095.7941729323, which is the exact answer.

This process of exploration shows that very accurate division is possible without progressive subtraction, and can give an accurate answer more rapidly in many cases. For this reason the method just described (although modified for use with binary numbers and using even better guesses at y_0) is widely used within computer systems for accurate division.

More important perhaps is that we have seen how problems can be tackled using a good first guess, based on research (in this case using the computer as our research tool) and then applying an iterative procedure that rapidly converges to the answer. This approach turns out to be very effective for a wide range of practical problems, some of which are simple, like accurate fast division or finding square roots, whilst other are far more complicated. And the process is related to a more general observation, that in such cases good experimental design starts with examination of the data, using this to obtain a good starting point, and then applying an efficient and appropriate procedure to home in on the desired result. To learn more about such problems, many of which come under the general heading of "Optimisation", see Walsh (1975).

11.3 Multiplication

We now look at $x=a*b$, where a and b may have a large number of digits. In the preceding sections we have assumed that multiplication is easy and fast, which in general is the case. But as with most questions of number manipulation, if there is a faster method of performing a calculation, especially one that is to be used very frequently, efforts to discover such procedures will be intense. One such method, which is also simple to appreciate for manual calculations, applies to multiplying any two large numbers together. At school this would have been described as long multiplication.

Let's take the example of 456 x 789. Instead of writing this as a set of completed sums, line by line (with carrying over each time, as in Table 11-2, diagram A), we can perform the carry over at

Table 11-2 Simplified carry for fast multiplication

A. Carry forward on each line						B. Carry forward at end					
			4	5	6				4	5	6
		x	7	8	9			x	7	8	9
		4	1	$_5$0	$_5$4				36	45	54
	3	6	$_4$4	$_4$8				32	40	48
3	1	$_3$9	$_4$2				28	35	42	
3	5	9	7	8	4		$_3$28	$_7$67	$_{12}$118	$_9$93	$_5$54
						3	5	9	7	8	4

the end and save time (as in diagram B); values carried forward are shown using subscripts.

In the second example, we ignore the need to carry forward the 5 from 54 to the second column until the end. We then add the 5 to the 93 on the line highlighted in grey to get 98, write down the 8 and carry the 9 which we add to 118 to get 127, write down the 7 and carry forward 12, and continue in this manner until the number is complete. This is quicker and less prone to error by hand, and provides the basis for much faster computations by computer. We can see how this works by looking at the example of vector multiplication we gave in Part I:

$$\begin{bmatrix} 4 & 5 & 6 \end{bmatrix}\begin{bmatrix} 9 \\ 8 \\ 7 \end{bmatrix} = 4*9+5*8+6*7 = 36+40+42 = 118$$

which is the middle sum of the five highlighted above. The rest of the five sums can be produced by shifting the 3 digits to be used for multiplication and zero padding these, as shown below, producing the result (before carry) in one matrix operation:

$$\begin{bmatrix} 4 & 5 & 6 \end{bmatrix}\begin{bmatrix} 7 & 8 & 9 & 0 & 0 \\ 0 & 7 & 8 & 9 & 0 \\ 0 & 0 & 7 & 8 & 9 \end{bmatrix} = \begin{bmatrix} 28 & 67 & 118 & 93 & 54 \end{bmatrix}$$

This operation can be implemented in computer software with far fewer steps than the conventional 'long multiplication' method, and therefore is widely used as the basis for fast multiplication of large numbers to arbitrary levels of precision. Using a technique known as the discrete Fast Fourier Transform (DFFT or DFT) such calculations can be performed at least 5x faster than direct multiplication, and 20+ times as fast for large numbers.

For more details on topics covered in this section, and scientific computing in general, see Conte and de Boor (1968) and Press et al. (1992).

12 EXPLORING NUMBER SERIES

12.1 Simple series

The sum $s=1+2+3+...n$ represents the sum of the first n Natural numbers. We can see that the set $\{s\}$ is a series that we can explore, as follows:

$s_1=1$
$s_2=1+2=3$
$s_3=1+2+3=6$
$s_4=1+2+3+4=10$
...

With the aid of our computer we can calculate this sum for any value n, for example $n=100$. Within Excel we could create a row of the form

	A	B	C	D	E	F	G	H
1	1	=A1+1	=B1+1	=C1+1	=D1+1	=E1+1	=F1+1	=G1+1
2	=A1	=A2+B1	=B2+C1	=C2+D1	=D2+E1	=E2+F1	=F2+G1	=G2+H1
3								

(only the entries in A1, A2, B1 and B2 are required, with the remainder being copied from B1 and B2). This gives us the number sequence we require in row 2:

	A	B	C	D	E	F	G	H
1	1	2	3	4	5	6	7	8
2	1	3	6	10	15	21	28	36
3								

We can extend the expressions in B1 and B2 by copying them across to column 100 (or column "CV" if your column headings are set to A, B, C... etc. as mine are above — the menu item Tools|Options, General tab allows you to change this to Row/Column numbered format, so A is labelled 1, B is labelled 2 etc.). In Column 100 we will have the value 5050.

If we factorise this number (e.g. using the Maple function, ifactor() or by hand) we find that $5050=2 \times 5^2 \times 101$ or $101 \times 100/2$. We might look at some of the other sums in our row to see whether a similar pattern exists. For example, for $n=50$ we see that $s=1275$, and this is $3 \times 5^2 \times 17$, or $51 \times 50/2$. What about an odd value, say $n=29$? The sum in this case is $435=3 \times 5 \times 29$ or $29 \times 30/2$. Maybe there is a general formula for this sum, $s=n(n+1)/2$? If so, then we can dispense with using a spreadsheet and evaluate the sum for any finite value of n, however large. So if $n=1000$ we expect to find $s=1000(1001)/2=500500$, which it does. We can check this by writing a small program or using the Sum() function in Maple:

z:=sum(k,k=1..1000); **500500**

However, because Maple is a symbolic processing language we can ask it to form this sum without specifying a number for *n*:

z:=sum(k,k=1..n); **(n+1)²/2-n/2-1/2**

The expression shown in **bold** type is Maple's attempt at finding a formula for the sum. Is it the same as ours? It looks more complicated, but if we ask Maple to simplify or factor the expression we get:

simplify(z); **n²/2+n/2**
factor(z); **n(n+1)/2**

which we see is the same as our formula — great!

The rather humbling part of this experiment is that the mathematician Gauss saw this result immediately when aged 10 during a school lesson. He got the answer by seeing that you can re-write the sum 1+2+3...100 in pairs as (1+100)+(2+99)+(3+98)... (50+51) and each pair adds up to 101, and since there are 50 pairs from 100 numbers, the answer must be 50*101=5050 — some people are just born smart! In fact, the problem that Gauss was set is believed to have been more general — it started at 81297 rather than 1, and increased in steps of 198 rather than 1. The general expression for such a sum, commencing with a value p and an interval *q*, can be determined from Maple in a similar manner to that above:

z:=sum(p+(k-1)*q,k=1..n); **pn + qn²/2 − qn/2**

If we were to try and sum the Integers for ever, i.e. to infinity, the sum would be infinite, but what about summing a series where each term is smaller than the last, for example 1/*n*? This is the series

$s_n = 1/1 + 1/2 + 1/3 + 1/4 ... 1/n$

Obviously as *n* gets larger and larger, 1/*n* get smaller and smaller, indeed becomes vanishingly small. As before we can calculate *s* for *n*=1, 2, 3... 100, 1000 etc. and see if there is a pattern. We get the results *s*={1,1.5,1.8888..., 5.187,...7.485,...} so it is not clear what is happening here. If we use Maple and specify 'infinity' as the upper limit, we find:

sum(1/n,n=1...infinity); ∞

so despite the fact that 1/*n* becomes as small as you like, the sum grows to infinity as *n* increases without limit, albeit very slowly. In fact it takes roughly 272 million terms before this sum even exceeds 20!

When n=100 we found s=5.187 and when n=1000 we found s=7.485. These totals could be of the form s=constant+(some function of n that increases very slowly). Now $\log_e(100)$=4.605... and $\log_e(1000)$=6.908... (i.e. using base e or natural logarithms), giving

s_{100}=5.187=4.605+0.582 and
s_{1000}=7.485=6.908+0.577.

We can check this using Maple for much larger values of n, and we find that for n=10,000 the constant part is 0.57727 and n=1,000,000 it is 0.577126...

z:=sum(1/n,n=1...1000000)-ln(1000000);
evalf(z); **0.57721616**

More generally, if we subtract $\log_e(n)$ or $\ln(n)$ from the sum s_n, the total does converge to a fixed value as n tends to infinity, which is known as Euler's constant, usually represented by the Greek symbol γ. It is thought that Euler's constant is Irrational, but this has not yet been proved.

If we ask the same question but using $1/n^2$, so each additional amount decreases more rapidly, we find another remarkable result (originally discovered by Leonard Euler in the 1700s):

sum(1/n^2,n=1...infinity); **$\pi^2/6$**

If we try using a larger Integer exponent, e.g. $1/n^3$ or $1/n^4$, we can be confident the series will sum to a finite number, since these ratios become smaller even faster than $1/n^2$. Curiously enough, we know that the sum for $1/n^m$ where m=2,4,6... (i.e. even values of m) is of the form $a\pi^m/b$ where a and b are Integers, but so far no-one has found a similar formula for odd values of m, like 3, 5 etc. You can test this out in Maple. For odd values of m, e.g. m=3, you will find the answer is given as $\zeta(3)$, pronounced zeta(3), which is just a shorthand notation for this sum. It is known that $\zeta(3)$ is Irrational (Apery, 1974) and is often now referred to as Apery's constant. More generally the series $\zeta(s)$ is known as the Riemann zeta function. You might also suspect, from the preceding discussion, that the sum of $1/n^m$ for n=1,2...infinity and $m>1$ is always convergent (tends to a finite number), but for $m\leq1$ is always divergent (tends to infinity), and you would be correct! More detailed discussion on series involving π is provided in Part III.

12.2 Log series and Mapping the World

12.2.1 Calculating logarithms
In Part I of this book I explained how to calculate logarithms using the very crude method of binary chop search. There is, however, a useful series expression for logs, which perhaps we could

use for calculations, as follows:

$$s_n = \log(1 + x) = x - \frac{x^2}{2} + \frac{x^3}{3} - \frac{x^4}{4} + .. + (-1)^n \frac{x^{n+1}}{n+1} + ... \text{ for } -1 < x \le 1, n = 0, 1, 2...\infty$$

This series was discovered by Niklaus Kauffman (1620-1687) and published by him in 1668 (he rather confusingly changed his name at some point to Nicolaus Mercator, mercator being the Latin for "merchant"). Newton had also obtained this result three years earlier. In this case the log is base e, rather than base10, and is sometimes written as ln(x) or $\log_e(x)$. This is the base that Napier originally used, and for this reason such numbers are often known as Napierian or Natural logarithms. There is a simple relationship between the two forms of logarithm:

$$\log_{10}(x) = \frac{\log_e(x)}{\log_e(10)}$$

so that if we know the value of $\log_e(10)$ we can convert between these two bases very simply. However, if we experiment with this series we find it converges very slowly indeed. For example, let x=1, so the first few terms of the expression give

$$s_0 = 1, \; s_1 = 1 - 1/2 = 1/2, \; s_2 = s_1 + 1/3 = 0.8333..., \; s_3 = s_2 - 1/4 = 0.58333...$$

and this series eventually will result in $\log_e(2) = 0.693147...$ but only after an enormous number of terms (even after 1000 terms it is not correct to 3 decimal places). But we can see a pattern in this series — from the start the series oscillates either side of the true value. This suggests that we could use successive sums to create a new accelerated series, which may converge much faster. There are several possibilities here: for example we could take the arithmetic mean (average) of 3 successive sums: $(s_0 + s_1 + s_2)/3 = s_1(1)$ and do likewise for $s_2(1)$ etc. generating a new series of sums which oscillate less and converge to the correct answer slightly faster. Indeed, we can repeat the same averaging process of the new series $s_1(1)$, $s_2(1)$, $s_3(1)$ etc. to yield $s_2(2)$, $s_3(2)$, $s_4(2)$ ... and so forth. More generally we can write:

$$s_n(k) = \frac{(s_{n+1} + s_n + s_{n-1})}{3}, \; k = 1,2,3...$$

where the terms on the right hand side of this expression are the sums obtained from the previous, i.e. (k-1)th calculation.

With 23 terms in the initial series and repeated summing and averaging we find $s_{11}(11) = 0.6931475...$, encouragingly close to $\log_e(2)$, but only after quite a large number of calculations. This arrangement can be improved by taking a weighted average, e.g. by weighting the middle value by a factor of 2 and dividing through by 4, but can an even better procedure be devised?

A much better acceleration procedure was devised by Alexander Aitken in 1926, although unknown to Aitken it had previously been discovered by a Japanese mathematician, Takakazu Seki

Kowa (1642-1708). Again we consider the sums $s_0=1$, $s_1=1/2$, $s_2=5/6$,... s_{n-1}, s_n, s_{n+1} ... and use a weighted combination of a sequence of three terms to provide a better estimate for the middle value. The adjustment proposed by Aitken is as follows:

$$s_n(k) = s_{n+1} - \frac{(s_{n+1} - s_n)^2}{s_{n+1} - 2s_n + s_{n-1}}$$

If we look at the first 3 sums: $s_0=1$, $s_1=1/2$, $s_2=5/6$ and we have a revised sum for s_1 as follows:

$$s_1(1) = s_2 - \frac{(s_2 - s_1)^2}{s_2 - 2s_1 + s_0} = \frac{5}{6} - \frac{(5/6 - 1/2)^2}{5/6 - 1 + 1} = 0.7$$

We can repeat this process for $s_2(1)$ etc., and we will get a new series of sums $s_n(1)$ that are much closer to the true result. However, as in our previous example, the same procedure can also be applied to these new sums to create a set $s_n(2)$, which provide a better approximation. I illustrate this in Table 12-1 for the initial sum to 9 terms, using Excel again to perform these simple computations for us.

The result converges to an excellent approximation of $\log_e(2)$, and if we want this in Common logs (i.e. base10) we can simply convert it by dividing our answer by $\log_e(10)$, which is 2.302585..., giving $\log_{10}(2)=0.30103...$, i.e. $2=10^{0.30103}...$ which is the value we found in Part I.

We can improve on this procedure still further by computing the series $\log(X)=\log((1+x)/(1-x))$ for $0<x<1$, which has two advantages: first, it enables logs to be computed for any positive number, X, since $X=(1+x)/(1-x)$ has values from 1 to infinity (the latter if x is close to 1); second, the series converges rapidly for a wide range of x. For example, if x=0.5, $(1+x)/(1-x)=3$ and with 11 terms the log is accurate to 7 decimal places, whilst with x=0.75 we can determine log(7) to within 1% with the same number of terms. With this model we have the following very simple series, ideally suited to computational use:

$$\log((1+x)/(1-x)) = \log(1+x) - \log(1-x) = 2(x + x^3/3 + x^5/5 + x^7/7...)$$

Table 12-1 Aitken acceleration of a slowly convergent series

n	s_n	$s_n(1)$	$s_n(2)$	$s_n(3)$	$s_n(4)$
0	1				
1	0.5	0.700000000			
2	0.833333	0.690476190	0.693277311		
3	0.583333	0.694444444	0.693105756	0.693148869	
4	0.783333	0.692424242	0.693163341	0.693146682	0.6931472
5	0.616667	0.693589744	0.693139901	0.693147354	
6	0.759524	0.692857143	0.693150829		
7	0.634524	0.693347339			
8	0.745635				

12.2.2 Mapping the World

This last expression, log(1+x)-log(1-x), has another less obvious use. It provides the framework for making a rather special map of the World — perhaps the most important kind of map ever produced. In the 16th century maps were an essential aid to navigation, but existing charts did not represent directions in a helpful manner. Ideally, for navigation, you would like to draw a straight line across your map from say Boston in New England to Bristol in England corresponding to the direction (or bearing or azimuth) you should sail. For a flat, rectangular paper map to have this property it is necessary for areas North and South of the equator to be stretched by an amount that compensates for the fact that on the Earth the lines of longitude (the North-South lines) converge at the poles. The amount of stretching required was identified by Gerhardus Krämer (1512-1594) by comparing the sizes of small areas of a paper globe at various points North of the equator. Krämer made paper globes commercially and knew that on the surface of such a globe (or the Earth) the area of a small roughly square region of 1 degrees latitude by 1 degrees longitude, is much larger at the equator than at say 60 degrees North (as we can see from the grid pattern in Figure 7.2). So he deduced that the amount of North-South stretching required to achieve correct directions on a flat map would have to correct for this variation.

For example, the map would need to ensure that the regions shaded in grey in Figure 12.1 (each covering 15 degrees of latitude and longitude in this example) are approximately equal in area on the Earth's surface, even if they look very different sizes on the final map. This form of map (or projection) solved the problem set by the navigators, because straight lines on the map are true bearings. Krämer was better known by his latinised name, Mercator (Krämer means grocer or merchant in German), so we call this kind of map a Mercator Projection, but he was no relation to

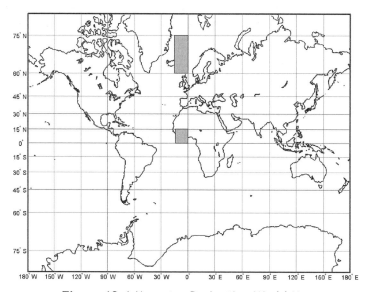

Figure 12.1 Mercator Projection World Map

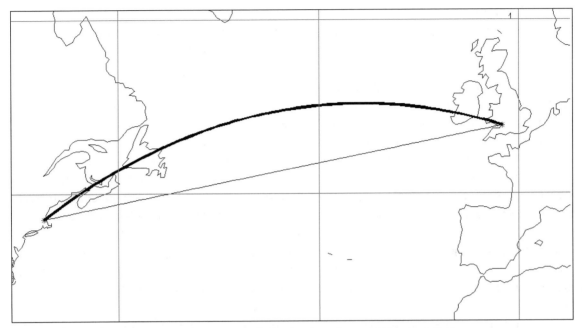

Figure 12.2 Boston to Bristol — Bearing and Shortest Path

the mathematician Nicolaus Mercator, who gave us the log series and was born a century later.

Note that on this World map the poles (90 degrees North and South) cannot be represented, and away from the equator the apparent size of regions like Greenland, Antarctica, Northern Canada and Siberia are greatly exaggerated — by 4 times at 60 degrees and by over 32 times at 80 degrees. Using Mercator's World Map we can now plot the sailing route from Boston to Bristol (Figure 12.2). The straight line shows the route, which is a constant bearing of 79 degrees from Boston, whilst the curved line shows the shortest path (a great circle), which is the route a modern-day jet would ideally follow (i.e. ignoring winds and air traffic controls).

These kinds of maps and calculations can be computed using spreadsheets coupled with manual or computerised drawings, but are far simpler to prepare with modern software tools such as Geographic Information Systems (GIS) or specialist mapping products. In the examples above I have used MATLab, with its optional *Mapping Toolbox*. All of the maps shown and calculations made were produced using fewer than 15 MATLab commands.

The precise amount of stretching required for Gerhardus Mercator's map surprisingly turns out to be based on Nicolaus Mercator's log formula. In this case

$$\frac{1}{2}\ln(1 + x) - \frac{1}{2}\ln(1 - x)$$

where x=sin(latitude). We can use this formula to calculate the spacing for the lines of latitude,

Table 12-2 Computation of Mercator Projection latitude line positioning, 1

Latitude	Lat (Radians)	x:sin(lat)	log(1+x)	log(1-x)	(log(1+x)-log(1-x))/2
75.00	1.309	0.96592583	0.6759633	-3.379	2.02759
60.00	1.047	0.86602540	0.6238107	-2.010	1.31696
45.00	0.785	0.70710678	0.5348000	-1.228	0.88137
30.00	0.524	0.50000000	0.4054651	-0.693	0.54931
15.00	0.262	0.25881905	0.2301740	-0.300	0.26484
0.00	0.000	0.00000000	0.0000000	0.000	0.00000

as shown in Table 12-2. From the equator at 0 degrees to 15 degrees North the spacing is 0.26 units, but from 60 to 75 degrees North it is 0.71 units, i.e. more than twice the separation.

Where did this magic result using logs come from? It is far from obvious, but a starting point is to look at Figure 12.3. We can see from this diagram that at the equator the radius of the Earth, R (from point A to B), is much larger than the radius, S, at latitude at 60 degrees North or South. So the length of the equator is 2πR kilometres and the length at 60 degrees North is 2πS kilometres, i.e. just simple multiples of the radii.

How long is S? The answer is simply Rcos(60°)=R/2. So if we want a small region (e.g. 1°x1°) at 60°N to represent the same area on the final map as a similar region at the equator, we must increase the height of our 1° wide rectangle at this point by 1/cos(60°)=2, i.e. we must double the height of a small region on the map at this latitude.

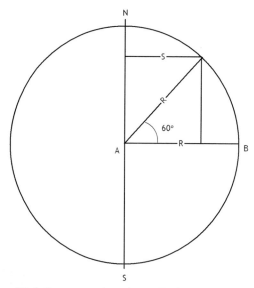

Figure 12.3 Cross-section through the Earth as a sphere

This still seems a long way from the complicated log formula we had, and anyway, the original Mercator (Gerhardus) didn't have the full benefit of this information or the methods needed to obtain it. What we now know is that at 1°N we must create a rectangle with height adjusted to 1/cos(1°), which is fractionally higher than 1 unit; at 2°N the next rectangle needs to be around 1/cos(2°) high; and so forth until we get to 60°N and beyond. As we stack these little rectangles on top of each other, each one slightly taller than the last, the total height at each point, e.g. every 5°N and S, should show the spacing for the lines on Mercator's final map.

Now we can calculate this sum of the heights of these small rectangles using a spreadsheet as before. In Table 12-3 we have taken θ=5 degree intervals, computed the 1/cos(θ) values (and multiplied each entry by the interval of D=5°). Column 4 sums the values as Sum(y) and column 5 shows the results from using the magic formula. The values in the two columns are quite close, and if we had taken D=1° or less the values would be very close indeed: the value of Sum(y) at 75°N with a 1° interval is 2.003 units and even closer, at 2.025 units with a 0.1° interval.

In this example we have added up, or numerically integrated, the expression 1/cos(θ). As with our earlier example involving gravitational acceleration (Section 3.5), if we take small enough intervals the sum (or integral) is found to be the magic formula we were looking for:

$$\frac{1}{2}\ln(1+x) - \frac{1}{2}\ln(1-x)$$

The full details are provided in Appendix 1 in the subsection on "Rates of Change, Mercator's map".

Table 12-3 Computation of Mercator Projection latitude line positioning, 2

Latitude	Lat (Radians)	y:1/cos(lat)*D	Sum(y)	(log(1+x)-log(1-x))/2
75.00	1.309	0.33717172	1.9116898	2.02759
70.00	1.222	0.25515007	1.6565397	1.73542
65.00	1.134	0.20649004	1.4500496	1.50645
60.00	1.047	0.17453293	1.2755167	1.31696
55.00	0.960	0.15214443	1.1233723	1.15423
50.00	0.873	0.13576252	0.9876098	1.01068
45.00	0.785	0.12341341	0.8641964	0.88137
40.00	0.698	0.11391828	0.7502781	0.76291
35.00	0.611	0.10653268	0.6437454	0.65284
30.00	0.524	0.10076663	0.5429788	0.54931
25.00	0.436	0.09628789	0.4466909	0.45088
20.00	0.349	0.09286703	0.3538238	0.35638
15.00	0.262	0.09034489	0.2634790	0.26484
10.00	0.175	0.08861269	0.1748663	0.17543
5.00	0.087	0.08759981	0.0872665	0.08738
0.00	0.000	0.08726646	0.0000000	0.00000

12.3   Trigonometric series

As with the computation of log(1+x) there are simple series expressions for sin(x), cos(x) and related functions. We shall just look at sin(x), since cos(x) can be determined from sin(x) using for example the relation sin(x+π/2)=cos(x).

The standard infinite series for sin(x) is:

sin(x)=x-x^3/3!+x^5/5!-x^7/7!+..., where -∞<x<+∞

from which we can immediately see that the expression oscillates as each additional term is added, much as log(1+x) did. If we compute the series for a few values of x, we find that it is unusable for general values of x, such as x=10. The same is true for the series representation of cos(x). The trick is to use the observation we made in Part 1 that sin(x)=sin(x+2π), so we can take any value of x, add or subtract 2π until it falls into the range [0,2π], say, and then use the series. As before, we can compute this series in Maple as follows:

```
x:=3:
z1:=sum((-1)^k*x^(2*k+1)/(2*k+1)!,k=0..12):
evalf(%); 0.014110008059867...
```

Here we have used 13 terms to obtain an estimate for sin(3) (i.e. the sine of 3 radians or about 171 degrees) to an accuracy of 15 significant digits. In fact with 13 terms this formula works well for x as large as around 9 or as small as -4, but after then it begins to fail. As long as we reduce x to a manageable range, and then use the series expansion with a reasonable number of terms (I suggest an odd number of terms), accurate results for sin(x) for any angle in radians can be generated, and from this cos(x) and sin(x)/cos(x) which is called tan(x) (tan being short for *tangent*).

12.4   Inverse Symbolic Calculation

Using Maple we have seen that the results of computations are given in symbolic form wherever possible. By this we mean that the software retains and uses symbols in preference to numbers when it provides answers, unless you explicitly request it to provide a numerical evaluation of an expression. But suppose that you have a number, such as x=1.6180339887, and are curious to see whether a simple expression or series results in this value. In other words, given a number, Integer or Real, can we do the inverse of numerical calculation and find a formula or symbolic representation?

The answer to this question will depend upon the number we are investigating, and how unique it appears to be. It is always possible that our sample number may be the result found from several different formulas. One way to test this idea is to use an Inverse Symbolic Calculator (ISC), an example of which is available on the web at the address:

http://www.cecm.sfu.ca/projects/ISC/ISCmain.html

If we enter the number for x above, we find about 20 different possible formulas, amongst which are: $x \approx (1+\sqrt{5})/2$ (which is the formula for the Golden Ratio, as discussed in Part III); and $x \approx 2\cos(\pi/5)$; in fact all the suggested formulas are equivalent, and we can be reasonably sure the expression we are looking for is the Golden Ratio. If we only knew x to 7 decimal digits some other possibilities would arise, for example x=10,000,000/6,180,341.

12.5   Random number generation

The final example in this section deals with the problem of generating a series of pseudo-random numbers. By definition this is a series of numbers that exhibits no discernable pattern, i.e. there is no way of predicting the next value having been given any number of prior values in the series and all possible numbers are equally likely to occur. The term pseudo-random is used to mean that the series is not truly random, since it is created by a well-defined non-random process, but it appears to be random.

The procedure I will describe is known as the linear congruence method and is essentially an iterative form of the standard equation for a straight line, $y=ax+b$. The procedure uses modular arithmetic and includes x on both sides of the equation for each iteration (n is the iteration number, $n=0,1,2,\ldots$):

$x_{n+1}=a*x_n +b \ (\mathrm{mod}\ m)$

where x_0 is the initial or seed value, a and b are constants, and m is a modulus value. Suppose we start with a=257, b=11, m=100 and x_0=59. We put these values into the iterative expression and this gives x_1=257*59+11(mod 100)=16174(mod 100)≡74 (which is the remainder after we divide 16174 by 100). If we put this expression into Maple (which conveniently provides modular arithmetic) we have something like:

```
x:=59:
a:=257:
b:=11:
m:=100:
```

% the next line defines f as a function of x

```
f:=x->a*x+b mod m:
```

```
for i from 1 to 10 do
    x:=f(x);
end do;
```

When this small program is run, we find that we get the sequence 59, 74, 29... until x_4=59, so the program repeats the sequence of 'random' numbers generated after only 4 steps, which is of no use. However, by careful selection of the values we use, the length of this sequence or 'perio-dicity' can be made very large. For example, using the values a=16807, b=0, m=2^{31}-1=2,147,483,647 and x_0=1, we find that the sequence has a period of 2^{31}-1 numbers, i.e. the same as m, which is much better!

Here is a sample of code for Maple that uses these values and outputs the pseudo-random numbers in an array or vector, *v*. Each random Integer is initially in the range [0,m] so we divide by m at the end to obtain a set of random numbers in the range [0,1]:

```
x:=100:a:=16807:b:=0:m:=2147483647:
f:=x->a*x+b mod m:
v:= array(1..10):
    for i from 1 to 10 do
        x:=f(x):
        v[i]:=evalf(x/m):
    end do:
print(v);
```

The resulting output is a set of 10 values, starting 0.00078, 0.15677,0.56053 etc. and these will always be the same each time the routine is executed, unless the initial value of x, the seed, is altered from 100 to some other value, as discussed earlier. Of course, Maple, like many other software environments, provides built in functions for both random number generation, the function rand(),) and for automatically changing the seed each time it is called, the function randomize().

13 POPULATION MODELLING

"When rapid growth occurs within an animal population it is referred to as 'disruption' to indicate clearly that the species has briefly escaped the control of the forces that maintain it in balance with its environment. In nature order is restored by a strong death rate, which returns the population to its habitual level. Sometimes the environment is irredeemably changed — as occurred with the introduction of dogs, rats and rabbits in Australia and the Pacific Islands — and a new balance is established between living species." Hervé Le Bras, in The Earth from the Air, Yann Arthus-Bertrand, 2002

Several of the techniques used in the previous section are examples of simple iterative algorithms. In this section we examine a variety of such methods and their application to population modelling and related processes. The results are surprising in two main respects: first, that fairly simple models can be used to describe quite complex patterns of growth and decline; and second, that seemingly inexplicable instability in population numbers and even extinction can arise through very simple models of reproductive behaviour.

13.1   Population growth models

When we looked at Earth's gravity in Part I we showed that the distance, d, covered as you fall can be described by the equation $d=gt^2/2+bt$, where t is time and b is a constant (your initial speed, which may be 0). We obtained this result by calculating the distance at time $t+1$ from the iterative expression, computed using an Excel worksheet, of the general form:

$d_{t+1}=d_t+v_t$

where d_t is the distance covered at time t, and v_t is the velocity at time t; $v_t=gt$ because of the constant acceleration assumption.

This is an incrementally additive function in terms of the distance at time t. At each point in time the distance is increased by an amount that grows linearly with time. A similar iterative expression, of wide applicability in modelling population (p), is one in which the population at time $t+1$ is a *multiplicative* function of its previous value. Such a model might be useful in calculating the growth of bacteria on a test dish or the growth of particular insect, fish or bird populations. In the following Sections we investigate a range of such models, which allows us to understand some of the complexity and unpredictability that exists in quite simple dynamic processes (processes that develop and change with time).

13.1.1 Simple population growth model

In its most basic form we have the following population growth or decline model:

$$p_{t+1}=(1+r)p_t \qquad \text{where we will assume } -1 \leq r \leq 1$$

Thus the population at time $t+1$ is a simple multiple of the population at time t. Since $p_{t+1}=(1+r)p_t$ is an iterative formula, we can write

$$p_{t+2}=(1+r)p_{t+1}=p_{t+2}=(1+r)(1+r)p_t=(1+r)^2p_t$$

or more generally $p_t=(1+r)^t p_0$. This is known as geometric or exponential growth and is essentially the same formula that is used in calculating the growth in value of an initial sum, p_0, if interest accrues at r% for t years (so-called compound interest).

To make this more tangible, suppose $p_0=10$ and $r=1$, then $p_1=20$, $p_2=40$, $p_3=80$... hence this is a very rapidly growing population, doubling each time period. A more realistic situation is to assume that r is a fraction less than 1, $r=$(birthrate%-death rate%)/100, and if births exceed deaths we have growth, or vice versa and we have decline. If the birth rate is 20 per 100 population and the death rate is 10 per 100 in any one period, we have $r=0.1$, and thus with $p_0=10$ as before, $p_1=1.1\times10=11$, $p_2=1.1\times11=12.1$, $p_3=12.1\times1.1=13.31$... We can easily generate this sequence in Excel and then plot the result for the first 40 time periods (see Figure 13.1). As can

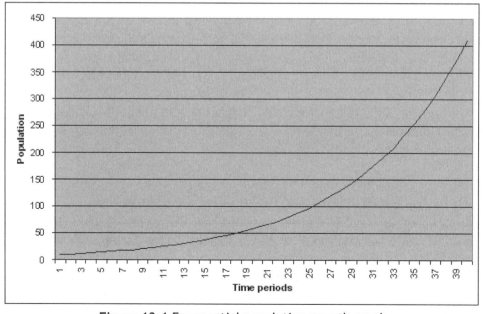

Figure 13.1 Exponential population growth graph

be seen, population growth is very rapid, doubling roughly every 7 time periods, and continues without limit, which is not very realistic.

A quick way of identifying whether the graph of a set of data is of this general form is to plot $\log(p_t)$ instead of plotting p_t directly (the base of the log() function does not matter, so log base10 or e are equally acceptable). If the result is a straight line the pattern can be described as geometric or exponential growth. Taking log values is also very useful when the vertical axis, in this case the one displaying p_t, has a very large range, extending over several orders of magnitude: for example, a plot of the quantity of a particular chemical compound in soil or air samples, where measured values range from 0.1 (10^{-1}) to 100,000 (10^5) parts per million. If $\log_{10}$ values are taken the amended data range will be from -1 to 5.

In the late 18th century the English economist Thomas Malthus (1766-1834) proposed the exponential process as a model of human population growth and argued that with food supplies only growing in a linear manner, mass starvation was inevitable and perhaps imminent. In practice population growth has not been exponential and food production has grown more than linearly, but on a global scale, especially taking into account differences in consumption and distribution of food, Malthus' warnings remain a significant concern.

A population model with more general applicability would take into account limitations on the food supply or predator-prey relationships, thereby limiting growth. Obtaining a reasonably realistic model in mathematical (equation) form is quite difficult, but there is nothing to prevent us from experimenting with assumptions and numbers. We will carry out experiments with two models: the first involves no predators but assumes that population growth eventually declines as the numbers increase (e.g. due to over-crowding of the available living space, social factors or limitations of food or other resources); the second is a more complex problem involving predators and prey.

13.1.2 Density constrained growth model
In simple exponential growth we worked with the formula $p_{t+1}=(1+r)p_t$, where r is a constant (r=birth rate − death rate). Our new model is actually the same, but with r changing over time as the population increases:

$$r_t=r_0(1-p_t/K)$$

where r_0 is the initial growth rate and K is the upper limit of population growth − for example, a constraint reflecting the "carrying capacity" of the land on which this population lives, or the available space on the dish containing a bacteria sample. As with the exponential model, you can readily generate the growth sequence using Excel. The cell entries in this case will be something like: =Bn*(1+$C$2*(1-Bn/$D$2)) for cell Bn, where n=2,3,4... and where C2 contains the initial rate, r, and D2 contains the population maximum, K (the $ symbol in Excel is used to indicate a fixed reference cell).

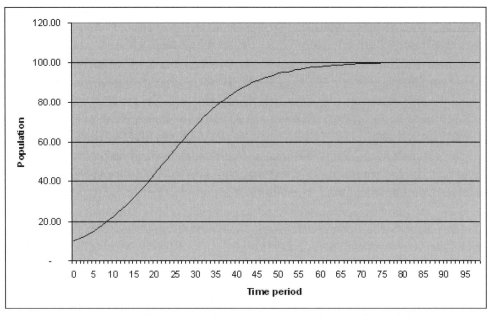

Figure 13.2 Logistic (density constrained) growth model

The graph in Figure 13.2 shows the impact of this modification where we have chosen r_0=0.1 as before and K=100. The result is growth constrained to the upper value, K, and the growth curve always displays this S-shape. The model has many applications, not just in population dynamics but also in quite different fields such as economics. It dates from 1838, being the idea of a Belgian mathematician Pierre Verhulst who developed it after reading about the ideas that Malthus published 4 years earlier, and is known as the logistic curve.

This curve has many applications, for example: it has been used to forecast the ultimate limits to world record times in sprint races; it has been used to model the 2001 foot-and-mouth epidemic and analyse why the spread of the disease was not handled more effectively; it has been applied to modelling government expenditure as a proportion of national income over time; and to model technological advances, reflecting a process of discovering and learning, through to fuller under-standing and development, leading to maturity in both understanding and product developments.

13.1.3 Predator-prey model

Suppose now that we have a simple combination of predators and prey, for example aphids and ladybirds (ladybugs), or herbivores and carnivores. We will assume that there are more prey than predators normally, and that prey have unlimited food supplies whilst predators simply eat prey. This model is rather more complex than those we have previously examined. It is known as a Lotka-Volterra problem, after the American and Italian scientists who made the most detailed analysis of such situations in the late 1920s. We need to specify the setup more formally. There are four parts to the process: the factors affecting the population growth of prey and predators; and the factors affecting population decline of prey and predators. The assumptions we shall make are as follows:

1. Prey, p, reproduce in proportion to their numbers, so their population increases exponentially at rate r_p unless checked, as we saw earlier: $p_{t+1}=(1+r_p)p_t$ or more simply $p_{t+1}=p_t+r_p p_t$

2. Prey numbers are reduced (they get eaten!) by predators, q, in proportion to both their own numbers *and* the number of predators. This can be represented by adding a single term: $-ap_t q_t$ to the expression for the number of prey, where 'a' is determined by the rate at which predators consume their prey. So for prey numbers over time, t, we have: $p_{t+1}=p_t+r_p p_t-ap_t q_t$

3. Predators die in proportion, b, to their numbers in the absence of enough food (prey), so their population decreases exponentially: $q_{t+1}=-bq_t$

4. Predators increase in proportion to both their numbers and the number of prey, so their population also increases exponentially at rate r_q unless checked: $q_{t+1}=q_t+r_q q_t p_t$. So for predator numbers we have: $q_{t+1}=q_t+r_q q_t p_t-bq_t$

So we now have the 4 factors expressed in two inter-related iterative expressions. As before, we can put these into an Excel sheet and explore what happens when we set different values for p_0, q_0, r_p, r_q, a and b. We can do this very simply, but as with our example in Part I of stepping out of a helicopter, we need to consider the patterns of growth and decline during the course of each interval. The easiest way to do this is to estimate values for $^1/_2$ way through each interval. In the example shown in Figure 13.3, the starting value for the prey population is 50, and for the predators, 15 (we can think of these as 100s or 1000s if necessary). The rate of prey population growth is r_p=10%, and for predators, r_q=0.1% of the *combined* predator-prey numbers. If there are insufficient prey the predators die out at a rate of b=5% and the prey are consumed at a rate of a=1% of the *combined* predator-prey numbers. So, if we ignore the $^1/_2$ interval problem initially, in time slot 0 to 1 the prey population *increases* by 10% by reproduction from 50 to 55, but over the same period *decreases* by 1%*50*15=7.5 as some are eaten. The net result is that the prey population *decreases* to by 2.5 to 47.5. The same pattern occurs for predators, but in the first period there is no net change in numbers (they increase by 0.75 and decrease by 0.75).

When you look at the table you will see that the actual numbers shown for time t=1 are slightly different: 47.56 for prey and 14.98 for predators. The reason is that I have adjusted these by evaluating the expressions at the mid-interval of the time slot and these calculations are shown in the second block of numbers, in italics. If all this seems a bit complicated, the details are provided in the sample spreadsheet that you can download from the web site associated with this book. What we can now do is plot the two columns shaded light grey to see how the predators and prey make out (Figure 13.4).

r(p)	r(q)	a	b
0.1	0.001	0.01	0.05

Time, t	Prey								Predators							
	Pop	+	–	Net	Pop*	+*	–*	Net*	Pop	+	–	Net	Pop*	+*	–*	Net*
0	50.00	5.00	-7.50	-2.50	48.75	4.88	-7.31	-2.44	15.00	-0.75	0.75	0.00	15.00	-0.75	0.73	-0.02
1	47.56	4.76	-7.13	-2.37	46.38	4.64	-6.94	-2.30	14.98	-0.75	0.71	-0.04	14.96	-0.75	0.69	-0.05
2	45.26	4.53	-6.76	-2.23	44.15	4.41	-6.57	-2.16	14.93	-0.75	0.68	-0.07	14.89	-0.74	0.66	-0.09
3	43.10	4.31	-6.40	-2.09	42.06	4.21	-6.22	-2.01	14.84	-0.74	0.64	-0.10	14.79	-0.74	0.62	-0.12
4	41.09	4.11	-6.05	-1.94	40.12	4.01	-5.88	-1.87	14.72	-0.74	0.60	-0.13	14.66	-0.73	0.59	-0.14
5	39.22	3.92	-5.72	-1.80	38.32	3.83	-5.56	-1.72	14.58	-0.73	0.57	-0.16	14.50	-0.72	0.56	-0.17
6	37.50	3.75	-5.40	-1.65	36.67	3.67	-5.25	-1.58	14.41	-0.72	0.54	-0.18	14.32	-0.72	0.53	-0.19
7	35.91	3.59	-5.11	-1.51	35.15	3.52	-4.96	-1.45	14.22	-0.71	0.51	-0.20	14.12	-0.71	0.50	-0.21
8	34.46	3.45	-4.83	-1.38	33.77	3.38	-4.69	-1.32	14.01	-0.70	0.48	-0.22	13.90	-0.69	0.47	-0.23
9	33.15	3.31	-4.57	-1.25	32.52	3.25	-4.44	-1.19	13.78	-0.69	0.46	-0.23	13.67	-0.68	0.44	-0.24
10	31.96	3.20	-4.33	-1.13	31.39	3.14	-4.21	-1.07	13.54	-0.68	0.43	-0.24	13.42	-0.67	0.42	-0.25

Figure 13.3 Predator-Prey population model

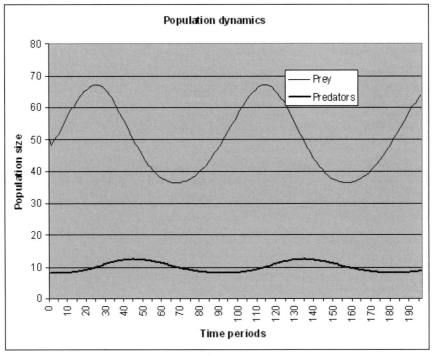

Figure 13.4 Graph of Predator-Prey model of population dynamics

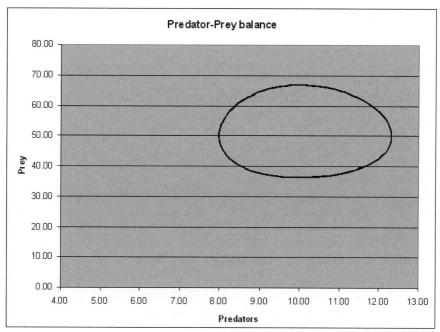

Figure 13.5 Predator-Prey balance

As can be seen, each population rises and falls over time in a regular manner, with a lag between them. The population of predators starts to fall after the prey population declines, and then picks up again once the prey have recovered their numbers. Obviously the specific numbers and the detailed pattern will vary according to the values of the 4 main rate variables (or *parameters*) r_p, r_q, a and b. To understand their effects we can change them systematically and, for example, look at the results if the predator growth rate r_q=0.25% instead of 0.1%. In this case the pattern remains the same but the predator numbers exceed prey for short periods, which is possible although a less likely scenario. All these patterns show curved profiles rather than straight line relationships, so we say they are *non-linear*, and they change over time, so we describe them as *dynamic*.

We can also plot the pattern of predators versus prey to see the balance ignoring time (Figure 13.5). This is a like a map because it is a 2D representation but not of a physical area, and the time value is effectively 'wrapped around' the closed circuit, running anti-clockwise. This kind of chart can be created in Excel using the X-Y scatter plot option using the same two columns of data and is sometimes described as showing *phase space* rather than physical space.

If the initial populations are altered but the rates are kept the same, there will be a pair of values (p,q) for which the predator and prey populations remain largely unchanged over time — this occurs at the centre of a series of closed curves like the one shown in Figure 13.5, in this case at about (50,10). This is called an equilibrium state. Some non-linear dynamic systems have points of equilibrium but many do not. They are, however, the norm for systems of the type we have just described. Frequently such systems show sudden changes of behaviour at critical values of the parameters, and whilst in the past such oddities tend to have been discarded as being rather uninteresting cases, in recent years they have attracted a great deal of interest, so I have included a brief discussion of such situations in the Section that now follows.

13.2   Recursion and chaos

13.2.1 Population models and chaos

A version of the logistic (constrained) population model was investigated in detail by Robert May, the former President of the Royal Society, in 1976. In Professor May's version, instead of

$$p_{t+1}=(1-p_t/K+r_0)p_t$$

which is the standard logistic model, he examined the equivalent model (known as the *Logistic Map*) in which $r_0=0$, $K=1$ and a rate multiplier, r, is introduced:

$$p_{t+1}=r(1-p_t)p_t \text{ where } r \text{ is a constant} >0 \text{ and } p_0 \text{ is in the range } 0<p_0<1$$

As before, we can set this expression up in Excel, and examine its behaviour for various values of r and p_0 over time. For example for cell A2 we might have the Excel expression =$F$1*A1*(1-A1) where A1=p_0 and cell F1 contains r. Copying this expression down column A gives a sequence over time, which we can then plot (Figure 13.6). In the diagram I have done this for an initial popu-

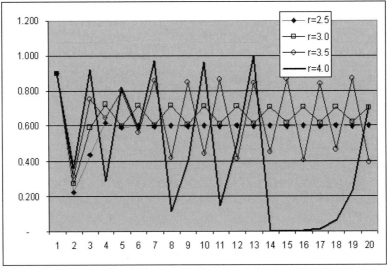

Figure 13.6 Logistic population model, chaotic effects

lation of 0.1 units, and rate values of $r=2.5$, 3, 3.5 and 4

What we see is that for $r=2.5$ the population value stabilises rapidly to a fixed value, rather like the classical logistic model. For $r=3$ and 3.5 the pattern is rather different, with continuous oscillation around a well-defined value. The oscillations for 3.5 are larger and more complex than those when $r=3$, and when $r=4$ (in fact when $r>3.570...$) the pattern breaks down and the oscillations are wild, unpredictable and chaotic. Changing the value of p_0 within the range specified has no material effect on these patterns, although quite complex variations do occur in the region of $r=3.5$.

> "What makes the Logistic Map fascinating to scientists is the observation that it can be applied successfully to ecology, the branch of biology that deals with the relations of organisms to one another and their environments. In particular, the map gives remarkable insights into changes in animal populations that take place over time. The spawning of salmon stocks, the number of ants crawling around their hill, even the fluctuations of grouse populations on moorland." Prof Robert May, in "It must be beautiful", G Farmalo (ed), 2002

This very simple recursive relationship exhibits very unexpected behaviour, and many natural systems, not just species populations, have been found to share some of these characteristics. For example, models designed for forecasting weather are often very sensitive to small changes in the input values. In broad terms, systems that are dynamic, highly sensitive to small variations in some initial values, and bounded (do not grow forever) may be classified as being chaotic. Strictly speaking there are some other, quite technical criteria for deciding whether a system is chaotic, principally relating to the exact behaviour of the outputs (the p_t values in our case) as the inputs are varied (r and p_0 in our case).

13.2.2 Complex variables and chaos

Amongst the most famous of chaotic sets is one discovered by Mandelbrot, some of whose work we have already discussed in connection with dimensionality. Before we describe this set and generate sample results using MATLab, we start by considering the very simple recursive procedure or map:

$x_{n+1}=k+x_n^2$ with $x_0=0$ and $k>0$

We can see that this is quite similar to the chaotic population model we have just examined:

$p_{t+1}=r(1-p_t)p_t=rp_t-p_t^2$

Indeed, if we set up an Excel spreadsheet with $k=-2$ we find the series for x becomes -2,2,2,2,... whilst with $k=-2.1$ it grows without limit, and for $k=-1.3$ it oscillates. Between around -0.9 and

152

+0.28 the values converge to a fixed number. Thus, depending on the input values, as before the system behaves in a very varied manner.

The Mandlebrot set is simply the set of values that k can take which are bounded (i.e. do not grow without limit). However, Mandlebrot permitted k to include complex numbers, z, as well as real values, and as we know from Part I, such numbers are actually pairs (x,y) which can be regarded as points on a plane, with axes x and y. In this case $z_0=(0,0i)$, and points in the set will satisfy -$2<|z|<2$. If we restrict ourselves to just a small part of this range, we can obtain an idea of the unexpected complexity of this set of numbers. In the picture shown on the rear cover I have plotted values from the set in the very small range $x=[-0.81453,-0.80989]$, $y=[-0.17602,-0.17138]$, using a grid resolution of 2000x2000 points (so 4 million pixels, if we regarded this as a digital photograph). The colours identify points in the set, with more intense colours highlighting areas containing the greatest number of points or detail. This sample section of the Mandelbrot set and also that used on the front cover were created using the MATLab software suite. More details on this set, together with free MATLab software with which you can explore this and many other forms of fractals, is provided on Laurent Cavin's website, listed at the end of this book.

The boundary of the Mandlebrot set is clearly a very complex and convoluted 'line'. In 1994 it was shown that this set does not have a dimension of 1, like conventional lines, but has a dimension (defined in terms of cover or capacity, as I discussed in Part I) of 2, so is essentially an area-like line.

14 CREATING NUMERICAL AND MATHEMATICAL DOCUMENTS

14.1 Word processing

Alignment and formatting of numbers and associated expressions and text is a very common requirement — whether this is for a marked assignment, a commercial report, a set of accounts, a thesis, a peer-reviewed paper or a book. In many cases such documents will be prepared largely within a word processing program, most frequently Microsoft Word at present. Alignment of columns of information is best achieved using tables in most cases, although embedded spreadsheets provide a widely used alternative. There are facilities within Word to provide 'decimal tabs', which ensures that the decimal points of a column of numbers always align, but these can be awkward to use. For more details on Word see the Format menu, Tabs... option, and/or click on the tab change icon in the top left of the page display area (the horizontal ruler) until the decimal tab icon is shown:

When typing expressions that involve the use of special symbols, not available in the basic ASCII set, or requiring augmentation of standard characters with special marks (like a line above or below), or complex positioning with respect to the normal text line (i.e. more than just superscripts and subscripts) additional software is generally required. For a word processing program such as Microsoft's Word product, an add-in is available called the Equation Editor. This enables complex expressions to be entered and effectively embeds the result as an object in the main body of the text, rather like inserting a diagram or picture. An enhanced version of this facility, known as MathType, is available as a commercial add-in, which supports a wider symbol range and exporting to TeX and other formats (see further, next section).

Microsoft Word does include facilities for creating very simple expressions, like 2/127x, using its Insert menu, fields option. For example inserting a field with contents: { EQ \f(2,127x) } can be used to create the fraction

$$\frac{2}{127x}$$

and { EQ \a \al \co2 \vs3 \hs3(A,B,C,D) } can be used to create the matrix

A B
C D

Creating the same symbols using the Equation editor is more straightforward, as these are edited directly, giving very similar results:

$$\frac{2}{127x} \quad \text{and} \quad \begin{array}{cc} A & B \\ C & D \end{array}$$

Far more complex expressions can be entered using the Equation editor, but full control of scientific expression entry and display requires the use of more sophisticated tools. A number of these are described a little later in this section.

Typewritten or printed numbers and expressions may also be subject to the conventions of national, international or specific publisher's preferences. Examples include: the use of commas, decimal points and other special symbols; in printed documents and reports it is normal to precede decimal fractions with a zero, i.e. 0.123 rather than .123; ranges of numbers are often abbreviated by omission of one or more digits, as in 167-168 being abbreviated to 167-68 or 167-8, but some number ranges should not be altered in this way, for example 11-13 should not be abbreviated to 11-3 and 115-119 should not be abbreviated to 115-9; it is important to ensure that it is clear from the context or expression that such expressions refers to a range and not a subtraction nor a backwards range (69-67 should always be written in full); in financial documents it is common to use the / symbol to indicate a financial year, as in 2001/2.

There is no international agreed standard for such issues, especially where numbers are embedded in text rather than within distinct equations, so care is needed and for published work, guidance from the publisher in question should be sought.

14.2   TeX, LaTeX and Moodle

14.2.1 TeX and LaTeX

TeX is a special-purpose programming language that is the centrepiece of a typesetting system. TeX produces publication-quality mathematics (and surrounding text) and is available to and usable by individuals rather than just typesetting experts. It was created in 1978 by the American computer scientist, Donald Knuth, and may be used for a wide range of complex document layout tasks, not just those involving numbers and mathematics. He himself said:

> "it is intended for the creation of beautiful books – and especially for books that contain a lot of mathematics".

LaTeX, which is widely used, is a set of extra facilities that extend some of the functionality of TeX, principally in the area of overall document structure.

TeX may be typed as a string of ASCII characters using a text editor, or may be generated by a number of specialised software tools designed for the creation of TeX format files (Figure 14.1).

TeX version	Typeset/layout version
Fermat's Last Theorem is defined as: \begin{equation} x^n + y^n \neq z^n \forall *n* \neq 2 \label{eq:fermat} \end{equation}	Fermat's Last Theorem is defined as: $x^n + y^n \neq z^n \ \forall n \neq 2$

Figure 14.1 Sample TeX extract

As with the web-oriented markup language, HTML, TeX can be typed directly but this does require detailed knowledge of the syntax and command set used.

Maple supports direct conversion of expressions to LaTeX and a range of other formats. For example, the expression we used in our discussion of Mercator's projection was:

$$\frac{1}{2}\ln(1+x) - \frac{1}{2}\ln(1-x)$$

and this can be converted using Maple's latex() command as follows:

latex(1/2*ln(1+x)-1/2*ln(1-x)); **1/2\,\ln \left(1+x \right) -1/2\,\ln \left(1-x \right)**

Instead of typing TeX directly, a purpose built editor can be used that supports TeX and related software by enabling information to be entered in a more visual manner. An example of such software, in this case based on a standard known as MathML (Mathematical Markup Language), is shown in Figures 14.2 and 14.3.

The first figure shows the result of simple on-screen editing using an extensive range of toolbars to insert special symbols, whilst the second shows the result in TeX format of the previous screen. This is rather like viewing the source for HTML that you have previously created in a purpose-designed HTML (web page) editor. Maple also supports conversion of expressions into MathML but tends to generate rather verbose output.

14.2.2 Web pages

Publishing numerical information and mathematical expressions on the web may be achieved in several ways. One of the most common is to use the built-in Table facilities provided in the HTML specifications and HTML editors. This will have a structure of the form:

```
<table border=1 cellspacing=0 cellpadding=0>
 <tr>
  <td width=284 valign=top style='width:213.05pt;border:solid windowtext .5pt;
  padding:0cm 5.4pt 0cm 5.4pt'>
.... more lines
  </td>
 </tr>
</table>
```

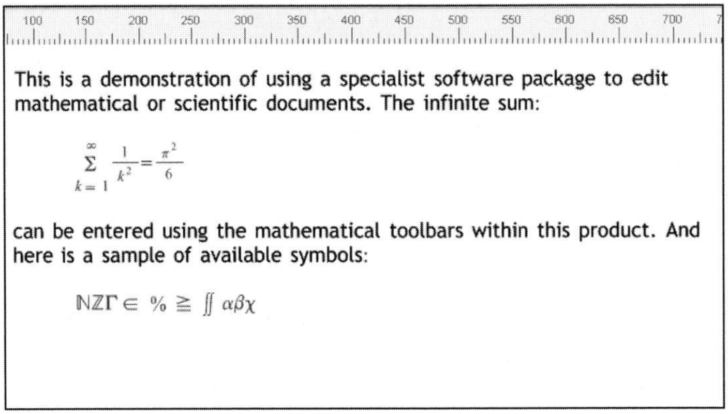

Figure 14.2 Mathematical editing using SciWriter

```
{
    \leftskip10mm \noindent This is a demonstration of using a specialist software package to edit
mathematical or scientific documents. The infinite sum:
}
    \EmptyParagraph
{
    \leftskip20mm $ \underset{{k = 1}}{\overset{{ \infty }}{ \sum }}\frac {{1}}{{{k}^{{2}}}} $=$ \frac
{{{{\mathrm{ \pi }}}^{{2}}}}{{6}} $
}
    \EmptyParagraph
    can be entered using the mathematical toolbars within this product. And here is a sample of
available symbols:
    \EmptyParagraph
{
    \leftskip20mm $ \mathrm{\mathrm{ \mathbb{N} }\mathrm{ \mathbb{Z} }\mathrm{ \Gamma }}
\in \% \geqq \iint \mathrm{ \alpha }\mathrm{ \beta }\mathrm{ \chi } $
}
```

Figure 14.3 TeX output generated from the above edited page

Of course, this simply provides aligned layout rather than an extended set of symbols. Where mathematical expressions and non-standard symbols are required within standard web pages these must either be provided as pictures (embedded image files) or an extension to the basic HTML specification is required, such as MathML:

"MathML is intended to facilitate the use and re-use of mathematical and scientific content on the Web, and for other applications such as computer algebra systems, print typesetting, and voice synthesis. MathML can be used to encode both the presentation of mathematical notation for high-quality visual display, and mathematical content, for applications where the semantics plays more of a key role such as scientific software or voice synthesis"

Yet another alternative is to create Portable Document Format (PDF) files using Adobe's Acrobat software suite (www.adobe.com) and enable access to these files using hypertext links within standard HTML web pages. For papers prepared using Word processors and typesetting systems this is frequently the best option, since the layout of the PDF file closely matches the original material, unlike web page presentation.

14.2.3 Moodle

Moodle is an OpenSource initiative (www.moodle.org) designed specifically for Educational use, primarily as a Course Management System. It provides a web-based interface for course materials, timetables, marking, tutor evaluations and much more. Moodle includes a TeX filter and a simpler, Algebra filter, for the creation of complex expressions within Moodle web pages and facilities. The TeX filter enables you to type in standard TeX within dollar signs, anywhere in Moodle (including forums etc.) like this:

$$ \Bigsum_{i=\1}^{n-\1}\frac1{\Del~x}\Bigint_{x_i}^{x_{i+\1}}\{\frac1{\Del~x} \big[(x_{i+1}-x)y_i^{5$\star}\big]-f(x)\}^\2dx$$

and it will be displayed efficiently like this:

$$\sum_{i=1}^{n-1}\frac{1}{\Delta x}\int_{x_i}^{x_{i+1}}\left\{\frac{1}{\Delta x}\big[(x_{i+1}-x)y_i*\big]-f(x)\right\}^2 dx$$

The algebra filter is similar but allows a more informal calculator-like notation within @@ characters:

@@cosh(x,2)-sinh(x,2)=1@@ , which is then displayed as:
$\cosh^2(x)-\sinh^2(x)=1$

PART III: INTERESTING NUMBERS AND SEQUENCES

This, the final Part of my exploration into the world of numbers and computation, provides a diversion from notation and applications. In it I look at some of these more 'interesting' numbers and number sequences. As I noted in Part I, it can be argued that all numbers are interesting, but some are more interesting than others. The following famous recollection relating to a visit to Ramanujan by Godfrey Hardy illustrates this vividly:

"I remember once going to see him when he was lying ill in Putney. I had ridden in a taxi-cab No. 1729, and remarked that the number seemed to me a rather dull one, and that I hoped this was not an unfavourable omen. 'No', he replied, 'it is a very interesting number; it is the smallest number expressible as a sum of two cubes in two different ways.' ... It was Mr Littlewood (I believe) who remarked that 'every positive integer was one of his personal friends'". G H Hardy

This recollection does not specify the exact date, although it must have been in either December 1918 or January 1919. The location was the Colinette Nursing home, 2 Colinette Rd, Putney, S W London. Records of pre-WW2 taxi licences issued no longer exist so checking some of the finer details of this story is not possible.

The picture above shows a London black taxi-cab of the period, although at the time many cabs were still horse-drawn 'Hansom' carriages (patented by Joseph Hansom in the 1830s), each uniquely identified by its 4-digit licence number (5 digit numbers are now used in London because there are more than 10,000 licensed taxis). The word 'taxi' is short for taximeter (a device invented in the 1890s to calculate the cost of journeys based on time or distance) and the word 'cab' is short for cabriolet, referring to the lightweight folding hood that provided protection for passengers from the rain. It seems almost certain that Hardy travelled in a motorised rather than horse-drawn cab as he uses the word 'taxi-cab'.

In that most famous of Sherlock Holmes mysteries, 'The Hound of the Baskervilles', John Clayton is described as driving cab number 2704 from Waterloo Station in hot pursuit of Henry Baskerville.

2704 is clearly a better candidate than 1729 for being described as numerically dull, apart from it being equal to 52^2. And in case you were wondering, the two cubes that sum to 1729 are 12^3+1^3 and 10^3+9^3. Strictly speaking this answer is not completely correct, since $91=3^3+4^3$ and $91=-5^3+6^3$, i.e. a smaller number is possible if we permit negative Integers.

Hardy asked Ramanujan at the time whether he knew the corresponding result for fourth powers, i.e. a number like $n=a^4+b^4=c^4+d^4$ where a, b, c and d are Integers. Ramanujan replied that he did not, but thought that the first such number must be very large. In fact this number had been found by Leonard Euler (1707-1783) and is indeed very large: $635,318,657=133^4+134^4=158^4+59^4$. In recent years there has been extensive research into numbers of this type, focusing on discovering the smallest numbers that can be expressed in exactly m ways as the sum of two numbers to the nth power. So, for example, if we use the notation Taxicab(n,m) as a general way of expressing such numbers, then:

Taxicab(3,2)=1729 (3rd power, 2 ways)
Taxicab(4,2)=635,318,657 (4th power, 2 ways), and
Taxicab(3,3)=87,539,319 (3rd power, 3 ways)

This last number was discovered in 1957 by John Leech (1926-1992). The three pairs of cubes are: 167^3+436^3, 228^3+423^3, and 255^3+414^3. The more general cases for 4th and higher powers, and for sums involving more than two terms, typically involve very large numbers indeed and at present even the existence of such 'smallest' numbers is not proven.

As with many topics involving the analysis of numbers, interest in such obscure and 'geekish' matters seems to have little value. However, as I have shown in Part II, such investigations may have practical value, for example in testing the numerical capabilities of computer systems; in leading to the development of better and faster computational and search algorithms; and even in identifying new ways of achieving secure communications.

15 NUMBERS

In the table at the end of this section I list a selection of numbers that have interesting properties or histories. Many of these are related to number sequences, which we cover in the second part of this Section. For clarity we refer to these sequences by name (e.g. Fibonacci, Fib for short) and number, to indicate the number in the sequence that they are derived from. Thus the third Fibonacci number is shown as Fib(3). In the case of Mersenne numbers we use this form of notation to indicate the nth Mersenne number, i.e. Mer(n), but we use Mer_p to indicate the pth Mersenne prime. The initial tabulated selection is shown in ascending numerical order for convenience. A much larger selection, which includes many of the numbers we have chosen to describe below, is contained in the *Penguin Dictionary of Curious Geometry/Numbers* by David Wells.

Several Real numbers warrant special attention, for example **π**, **e** and the constant known as the Golden Ratio. These are perhaps the most important and well-known mathematical constants, and entire books and websites are devoted to their properties, origins and applications. Because this is not a mathematics textbook I will not dwell on the many aspects of these numbers, but will focus instead on a selection of ways in which they arise in practical problems and how their values may be calculated.

Many phrases and poems have been devised over the years to act as a memory aid for the digits in such numbers. These are known as *mnemonics*, and the number of letters in each word in the phrase identifies the relevant digits of the number in question. For example: for the constant **e**, the phrase

"It enables a numbskull to memorise a quantity of numerals"

means 2.718281828, the first 10 digits of this constant; whilst the phrase

"How I wish I could calculate pi"

is a mnemonic for the first 7 digits of π.

15.1 Pi (π, 3.14159265...)

"What good is your beautiful investigation regarding π? Why study such problems, since Irrational numbers do not exist?" Leopold Kronecker, 1882

From a letter to a colleague who shortly afterward proved that π was not only

Irrational but also transcendental. Kronecker was a distinguished but very contro-versial mathematician because he believed all mathematics should be reducible to a study of the Integers and operations involving a finite number of steps (i.e. excluding the idea of infinities and infinite series). It is interesting to compare his views with the use of numerical methods in this book, since the latter are intrinsically finite. To this extent, as with Kronecker's views, the use of computational methods alone has well-defined limitations.

More has been written about the number π (sometimes referred to as Archimedes' constant) than perhaps any other in history — entire books and even films exist on the subject! Pi is most frequently encountered as a constant in the formula for the circumference C of a circle, radius r: $C=2\pi r$ or $C=\pi d$, where d is the diameter; and in the formula for the area of a circle: $A=\pi r^2$. If one wished to construct a square of the same area as a circle it would have side lengths $r\sqrt{\pi}$ and since we now know that π is Irrational, such a square cannot be constructed precisely. In March 2004 the British autistic savant Daniel Tammett memorised the first 22,500 digits of Pi and then spent five hours reciting them to an independent adjudicator. As he said at the time "I am technically disabled. I just wanted to show people that disability needn't get in the way." His feat is not the greatest number of digits memorised and recalled — that strange honour falls to Hiroyuki Goto from Japan who recalled over 40,000 digits of Pi in 1995.

From around 2000 BC onwards estimates of π were produced, since these were needed in prac-tical problems of construction. A very good ancient estimate — Egyptian, recorded in the Rhind Papyrus, dating from almost 4000 years ago — was $(8d/9)^2$ where d is the circle diameter. If we write $d=2r$, this gives $256r^2/81$ or roughly $3.16r^2$, i.e. π ≈ 3.1605. The Greek symbol π was not used by the Greeks or the Romans, but was introduced into general use by an English mathe-matician, William Oughtred, around 1650 and as shorthand for the word "periphery" (περιφερια in Greek) by a Welsh mathematician, William Jones, in 1706. Oughtred was also responsible for the introduction of x as a symbol for multiplication.

It is possible to estimate the area of a circle, and hence determine π (from the formula $A=\pi r^2$), by counting the number of small square tiles that would be required to fill a large circle (Figure 15.1). Suppose we have a square region, 19x19 tiles in area, within which we have an inscribed circle. We could calculate the distance from the middle of each tile in the large square to the central tile, and if this distance was less than or equal to 9 (our circle radius) we include it in our area estimate. We now count up the tiles that meet this criterion, and we find in the example shown (tiles highlighted in grey) that there are 253 in total. Since our radius is 9, the estimate for π=253/81=3.123 (close to the value 256/81 known to the Ancient Egyptians). Not very good, but then our approximation to a circle is far from perfect. If we could use many more tiles the errors due to the rough edge approximation would be far less: with a square region of 1001x1001 tiles and no edge adjustment the estimate is 3.14144; and with 10001 tiles per side the estimate is 3.141588. These results were computer generated, and are still poor considering the last *figure*

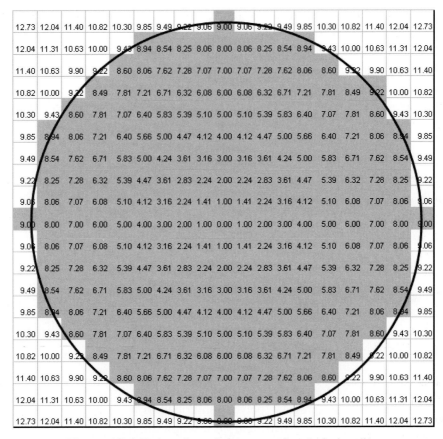

Figure 15.1 Estimation of the area of a circle by tiling

might involve millions of calculations — simply counting square tiles or points is not a practical process.

The best early estimates for π were made based on approximating a circle by a many-sided regular polygon inscribed within the circle. Regular n-sided polygons can be seen as collections of *n* triangles, each one with its point or apex at the polygon centre (Figure 15.2). The area of these triangles (which are all alike) is simple to calculate (e.g. using the rule that the area of a triangle is its height, *h*, times one half its base length), so the area of a regular polygon with n sides is simple to calculate. As the number of sides, *n*, is increased the polygon area will approach that of the circle.

For example, a 6-sided polygon (a hexagon) consists of 6 triangles, each of which has all their sides the same length, *r*, as shown in Figure 15.2. So each has an area $a=rh/2=r^2\sqrt{3}/4$ (because $h=r\sqrt{3}/2$) and thus 6 have an area $A=6r^2\sqrt{3}/4\approx2.6r^2$, and a perimeter of $P=6r$, giving estimates of

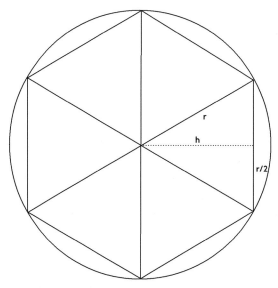

Figure 15.2 Hexagon (6-sided polygon) inscribed within circle, radius r

2.6 and 3 for π. With a 12-sided polygon the area is $A=3r^2$ and with 360 sides $3.14r^2$.

We can perform these calculations very rapidly using the standard trigonometric formulas for the area, A, and perimeter, P, of a regular polygon inscribed in a circle of radius $r=1$. The Excel formulas we need are: =n/2*sin(2*pi()/n); and =n*2*sin(pi()/n) where n is a cell reference (e.g. A2) of the number of sides, as shown in Table 15-1. As can be seen, this process requires use of a polygon with almost 100,000 sides before it is correct to 10 digits.

Table 15-1 Estimation of Pi by polygon approximation to a circle

Sides	Area, A	Perimeter/2, P/2
6	2.59807621135	3.00000000000
12	3.00000000000	3.10582854123
24	3.10582854123	3.13262861328
48	3.13262861328	3.13935020305
96	3.13935020305	3.14103195089
192	3.14103195089	3.14145247229
384	3.14145247229	3.14155760791
768	3.14155760791	3.14158389215
1536	3.14158389215	3.14159046323
3072	3.14159046323	3.14159210600
6144	3.14159210600	3.14159251669
12288	3.14159251669	3.14159261937
24576	3.14159261937	3.14159264503
49152	3.14159264503	3.14159265145
98304	3.14159265145	3.14159265306

In 1593 a French mathematician, François Viète (the person who introduced the decimal point into common usage), investigating this approach discovered the following unusual relation:

$$\frac{2}{\pi} = \sqrt{\frac{1}{2}} \times \sqrt{\frac{1}{2} + \frac{1}{2}\sqrt{\frac{1}{2}}} \times \sqrt{\frac{1}{2} + \frac{1}{2}\sqrt{\frac{1}{2} + \frac{1}{2}\sqrt{\frac{1}{2}}}} \times \dots$$

This is the first known example of an infinite product (multiplications) being used in mathematics. With the three terms shown it gives an estimate for π as 3.121..., but it is rather complicated and unwieldy in this form for practical use. However, using this formula an iterative procedure (sometimes called an Arithmetic Geometric Mean, or AGM procedure) can be produced to compute π quite accurately. For clarity we will use an Excel spreadsheet to illustrate this procedure (see Table 15-2), but it can be programmed in a few lines of Basic or most other languages very simply. We start by setting the initial values $x_0=1$ and $y_0=\sqrt{2}$. We then calculate new values for x and y from these, such that $x_1=x_0 y_0$ and $y_1=\sqrt{(2y_0/(y_0+1))}$. In Excel these expressions are shown next to Column B in Table 15-2.

Having created these expressions as the formulas in positions B3 and B4 you can simply select and copy them down as many rows as you wish — I have copied them to iteration 10. Column C shows the value of π as 2 times the value of x_i, so by iteration 10 we find π=3.141591422, which is accurate to 5 decimal places.

Table 15-2 AGM estimation of Pi

	A	B	Excel formulas	C (π estimate)
1	x0	1.000000000	=1.0	=2*col B x-values
2	y0	1.414213562	=sqrt(2)	
3	x1	1.414213562	=B1*B2	2.828427125
4	y1	1.082392200	=SQRT(2*B2/(B2+1))	
5	x2	1.530733729	=B3*B4	3.061467459
6	y2	1.019591158	etc.	
7	x3	1.560722576		3.121445152
8	y3	1.004838572		
9	x4	1.568274245		3.136548491
10	y4	1.001205996		
11	x5	1.570165578		3.140331157
12	y5	1.000301272		
13	x6	1.570638625		3.141277251
14	y6	1.000075304		
15	x7	1.570756901		3.141513801
16	y7	1.000018825		
17	x8	1.570786470		3.141572940
18	y8	1.000004706		
19	x9	1.570793863		3.141587725
20	y9	1.000001177		
21	x10	1.570795711		3.141591422
22	y10	1.000000294		

A much simpler series was discovered by the English mathematician, John Wallis, in around 1655. This is the infinite product:

$$\frac{\pi}{2} = \frac{2x2x4x4x6x6x8x8..}{1x3x3x5x5x7x7x9...}$$

If we calculate this product using 1,2,3... etc. terms in the top and bottom of the expression we find that it only converges to 3.14159... very slowly, and oscillates about this value, as shown in Figure 15.3. For this reason it is another interesting, but not immediately useful result.

A few years later, in 1678 the German diplomat and scientist Gottfried Wilhelm von Leibnitz (1646-1716) discovered a simple additive series for π, as:

$$\frac{\pi}{4} = 1 - \frac{1}{3} + \frac{1}{5} - \frac{1}{7} + \frac{1}{9} - ...$$

which is even simpler to compute, but again converges fairly slowly. This is because it requires roughly 50 terms before we are adding and subtracting fractions like 1/100, i.e. changing the result by 0.01. Of course, we could apply Aitken's acceleration procedure to this series (or the previous one) and doing so we obtain a value that is correct to 7 decimal places using only 7 terms of the Leibnitz series.

In recent years new formulas and procedures have been discovered which converge very much faster and the value for π has been computed to millions of decimal places. One of the simplest,

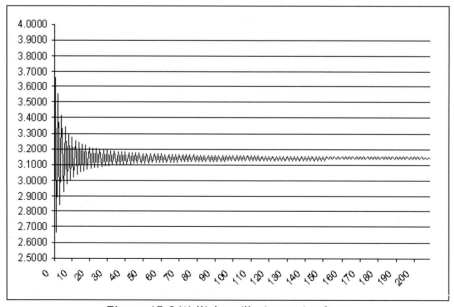

Figure 15.3 Wallis' oscillating series for π

Table 15-3 Fast AGM approximation for Pi

Iteration	Values	π estimate
x0	1	
y0	0.707107	
z0	0.50	
x1	0.853553	3.187672643
y1	0.840896	
z1	0.457107	
x2	0.847225	3.141680293
y2	0.847201	
z2	0.456947	
x3	0.847213	3.141592654
y3	0.847213	
z3	0.456947	

discovered in 1976, is another AGM-type iterative procedure. We start by setting three initial values $x_0=1$, $y_0=1/\sqrt{2}$ and $z_0=1/2$ — quite similar to our previous example of such iteration. We then calculate new values for x, y and z from these, such that $x_1=(x_0+y_0)/2$ and $y_1=\sqrt{(x_1y_1)}$ and $z_1=z_0-2^1(x_0^2-y_0^2)$ and repeat this pattern for subsequent iterations. The estimate for π is then calculated as $2x_i^2/z_i$.

If we create a simple spreadsheet with this new procedure we see a quite different result — with only 3 iterations the estimate is accurate to 9 decimal places (Table 15-3).

There are several algorithms similar to this now in use. In the example we have just shown, the number of digits correctly represented doubles every iteration, so within 10 iterations we can generate π accurately to over 1000 decimal places. It should be noted that both of these procedures assume that you can compute square roots to an arbitrary degree of accuracy first. Using new algorithms between 1998 and 2000 a network of 1734 computers computed the quadrillionth bit of π (i.e. represented in binary) and found it to be 0. Whilst this is an interesting result, it has very limited usefulness other than to test computer algorithms.

15.2 *e* (2.7182818285...)

The remarkable constant known by the letter **e** was originally discovered by Napier in 1618 during his work on logarithms. However, it was not until 1690 that it first appears explicitly, at which time is was referred to as **b**. During Euler's investigation of infinite series he introduced the same value and in a letter of 1731 called it **e**, the naming that remains to the present day.

Perhaps the simplest way of arriving at this constant is to consider the payment of interest on a loan. Suppose you borrow £1000 and have to repay this plus an amount of interest which is, say

Table 15-4 Approximation of *e*

n	1/n	(1+1/n)	$(1+1/n)^n$
1	1.00000	2.00000	2.00000
2	0.50000	1.50000	2.25000
3	0.33333	1.33333	2.37037
4	0.25000	1.25000	2.44141
5	0.20000	1.20000	2.48832
6	0.16667	1.16667	2.52163
7	0.14286	1.14286	2.54650
8	0.12500	1.12500	2.56578
9	0.11111	1.11111	2.58117
10	0.10000	1.10000	2.59374
100	0.01000	1.01000	2.70481
1000	0.00100	1.00100	2.71692
10000	0.00010	1.00010	2.71815

10% per annum, i.e. 1/10 times the initial sum. The total to repay would be the original sum plus £100, or £1000*(1+1/10)=£1100. If you did not repay this in year 1, and the sum was carried over to year 2, you would have to pay £1100*(1+1/10)=£1210. But by replacing the £1100 in this expression by the initial expression we see that this is simply £1000*(1+1/10)². Over 10 years the sum due would therefore be the initial sum times $(1+1/10)^{10}$. Keeping this expression but replacing the number 10 with any positive Integer, *n*, we have $(1+1/n)^n$, which is the amount we would pay over *n* years at 1/*n* interest. As the number *n* becomes larger, as shown in Table 15-4, this expression tends to a fixed number, 2.7182818..., which is known as the constant *e*. So no matter how many years over which interest accrues, if the interest rate matches the number of years then you will only ever owe 2.718... times the original sum.

This behaviour of the series $(1+1/n)^n$ as *n* becomes large is very similar to the behaviour of our Malthusian or exponential population growth model, where we had $p_t=(1+r)^t p_0$ and *r* is a fraction. In this case, if we reduce the size of the time intervals, *t*, by a factor *n* we increase the number of steps from *t* to *nt*, and we must also reduce the rate *r* in proportion, say by a factor *n* to *r/n*. Now we return to our population model:

$p_t=(1+r)^t p_0$, taking small steps we have
$p_t=(1+r/n)^{tn} p_0$, now let $r/n=1/N$, so we have $n=rN$ and
$p_t=(1+1/N)^{rtN} p_0$, so rearranging we have
$p_t=[(1+1/N)^N]^{rt} p_0$, and as $N \rightarrow \infty$ using our earlier result we have
$p_t=e^{rt} p_0$

This final expression is based on assuming N→∞, so we have p_t is approximately equal to $e^{rt}p_0$ for large numbers of small time steps — hence the term "exponential growth" (in Excel use =exp(x) to obtain the exponential of *x*, so if *x*=1 exp(1)=e=2.718...).

There is an interesting result we can deduce from this expression. We now know that it provides an estimate of the number or size of things after t time periods when growth is a simple function of the previous value — e.g. for population or invested income. How long will it be before the population doubles? or your initial investment or debt doubles? Well, this is simply the time t when $p_t = 2p_0$ thus $2 = e^{rt}$. But we want t, and the easiest way to obtain this is to recall that exponentials and logarithms are related, so we can rewrite this as $\log_e(2) = rt$ and thus $t = \log_e(2)/r$. We can find the value of $\log_e(2)$ from tables, a calculator or Excel (in Excel use =ln(2) for base e logs), and we obtain 0.69... . Now if r is a fraction between 0 and 1, e.g. $r = 0.1$ we would have $t = 7$ to one decimal place, and this is sometimes known as "the rule of 7". The number of intervals required to double your money or a population under these assumptions is roughly 7, i.e. 7 years if we have annual interest at 10%, or 7x2=14 years if interest rates are only 5% (0.7/0.05). If the annual percentage interest rate (APR) on a loan or credit card was much higher, say 35%, the debt would double every two years unless all or part of it was paid off rapidly (see Box 8 if you think that this is unlikely to happen!).

The limit value process is only one way in which the constant **e** arises — there are very many others. One example is as the sum of the infinite series, discovered by Euler:

$$e = 1 + \frac{1}{1} + \frac{1}{2.1} + \frac{1}{3.2.1} + \frac{1}{4.3.2.1} + \ldots = \frac{1}{0!} + \frac{1}{1!} + \frac{1}{2!} + \frac{1}{3!} + \frac{1}{4!} + \ldots$$

where the convention is that 0! is defined as 1. Table 15-5 shows the result of computing this expression for the first 10 elements, giving a value of 2.71828, i.e. rapidly converging on the true value:

The value **e** arises in many unexpected circumstances, for example as in the game of

---

Box 8. £384,000 debt mountain from £5,750 loan

A Merseyside couple whose mountain of debt was wiped out by a judge yesterday said that they felt as though a tonne weight had been lifted from their shoulders. Tony and Michelle Meadows had faced losing their home at Southport after they were taken to court for failing to keep up with repayments on their loan, which had an APR of 34.9 per cent.

Mr Meadows, 45, a car windscreen salesman, said after Judge Nigel Howarth's ruling at Liverpool Crown Court: "We are absolutely delighted. You can see the effect this has had on me — I used to have dark hair."

Mr and Mrs Meadows took out the £5,750 home improvement loan in 1989. Within months they began to struggle to keep up with payments. The original loan escalated to 67 times its original amount, to £384,000, through late payment charges, interest and legal costs.

Source: *The Times*, October 29th, 2004

Table 15-5 Series approximation of e

n	n!	1/n!
0	1	1.00000
1	1	1.00000
2	2	0.50000
3	6	0.16667
4	24	0.04167
5	120	0.00833
6	720	0.00139
7	5040	0.00020
8	40320	0.00002
9	362880	0.00000
10	3628800	0.00000
	Total	2.71828

"coincidence" or Treize (the French for 13). The chance that a card from a well shuffled set of 13 will not show the same face value (e.g. 7) as its *position* in the shuffled set (e.g. when the cards are turned over in sequence, 1, 2, 3...) is 1/e, or around 37% — put another way, the chance of a 'coincidence' is 63%.

It is useful to recognise that the series expansion for **e** given above is actually the expansion for **e**^{1}, and if we want to evaluate **e**^{x}, where x is some other value than 1, then we use the more general form:

$$e^x = 1 + \frac{x^1}{1} + \frac{x^2}{2.1} + \frac{x^3}{3.2.1} + \frac{x^4}{4.3.2.1} + \dots$$

Before concluding this section there is one truly remarkable and unexpected relationship between π, e and the imaginary value **i**, which was discovered by Euler. This is the equation e$^{i\pi}$=-1, showing that the three most interesting numbers are intimately connected. Demonstrating that this relationship is true is quite straightforward, but lies outside the scope of this book. Suffice it to say that it is an outcome of the fact that both π and e can be expressed as simple series, as shown above, and both are related to trigonometric series.

15.3 Golden ratio (Golden section) and Fibonacci series

"Without measurement, there can be no art", Divina proportione, Luca Paccioli, 1509

The Golden Ratio (also known as the golden proportion or golden section) is a number known since ancient times. It occurs widely in natural forms (flower petal arrangements and certain seashells for example) and has been used extensively in art and architecture because it is felt to be 'pleasing' to the eye. It has also been found to be closely related to simple growth processes (which explains its widespread occurrence in the natural world) and to certain well-known number sequences such as those of Fibonacci (the 12th century Italian mathematician whom we profiled in Box 3).

We can start by constructing the Golden Ratio geometrically. To do this we form a rectangle, as follows: first we draw a square, with side length 1 (Figure 15.4A). We then take a point half way down one side (point b) and draw a line to one of the opposite corners (Figure 15.4B). This gives a triangle, with base 1 unit and shortest side 1/2 unit, and therefore its longest edge (hypotenuse)

is $\sqrt{1+\frac{1}{4}}=\frac{\sqrt{5}}{2}$ units in length.

We now add half this length to one edge of the square to form part of a rectangle, which we then complete (Figure 15.4C and D). You can imagine doing this by swinging the line from b around until it aligns with the edge of the original square, as shown. This rectangle has sides 1 and

$$\frac{1+\sqrt{5}}{2}=1.61803..$$

which is the value known as the Golden Ratio.

The shape so formed is known as a golden rectangle, and consists of two parts, one of which is rectangular (Figure 15.4D) and the other is the original square (Figure 15.4C). If we now divide

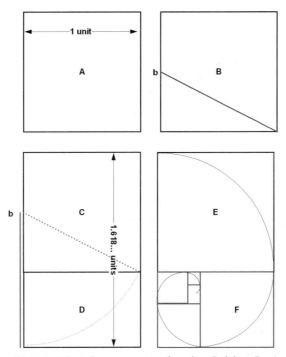

Figure 15.4 Construction for the Golden Ratio

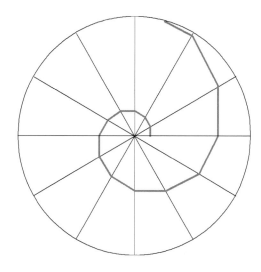

Nautilus shell — cross section   Spiral growth — 12 segment

Figure 15.5 Golden ratio growth patterns

this new smaller rectangle into two parts, using the same proportions, we obtain another, smaller golden rectangle. This process can be continued forever, so is another example of an iterative or repeated process.

A smooth curve can be drawn through the square parts of this sequence of divided rectangles, as shown in the last section of these diagrams (Figure 15.4E and F). This curve is known as a logarithmic spiral and is familiar as the cross-sectional shape of some shells, such as that of the nautilus (Figure 15.5, left).

I noted at the start of this sub-Section that the Golden Ratio is related to quite general growth processes, and the growth of natural objects may reflect this. So can we describe such processes? If we start with the example of a growth spiral, we can imagine a circle divided into an even number of sections, with growth from one section to the next being at right angles to the initial surface (Figure 15.5, right). If we increase the number of divisions so that the growth process becomes more and more smooth, the resulting curve is the same log spiral as before. Similar patterns are exhibited by the growth of leaves around plant stems, and seed growth in the heads of plants such as sunflowers.

I also noted earlier that the Golden Ratio is associated with the Fibonacci series, itself a form of growth process. When Fibonacci described the series originally he gave the example of pairs of rabbits, reproducing to produce another pair each month, with each new pair taking a month before they started breeding themselves. This generates the series: 1 (pair of rabbits), 1 pair, 2

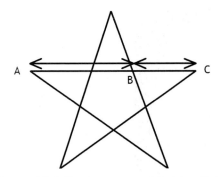

Figure 15.6 Pentagram and Golden Ratio

pairs, 3 pairs, 5 pairs, etc. The relationship is a very simple one. If Fib(n) is the nth Fibonacci number, then Fib(n+1)=Fib(n)+Fib(n-1), e.g. 5=3+2. If we calculate the ratio Fib(n+1)/Fib(n) we find it rapidly tends to the Golden Ratio as n increases in size. For example, F(11)/F(10)=89/55 is already very close at 1.61818. Surprisingly, this series and the associated ratio provides an efficient method for searching ordered sets of data (better than the simple binary chop), and in the era of magnetic tape usage was a widely used procedure for locating information on these tapes. Another, very simple geometric construction that exhibits the Golden Ratio is the Pentagram, a 5-pointed star (Figure 15.6). This figure has been important since ancient times as an occult symbol and was therefore studied and revered greatly. In this case the ratio AB:BC is 1:61803...:1.

Finally, as we saw in Part II, we can use a calculator or spreadsheet to calculate the approximate value of the simplest continued fraction possible:

$$1 + \cfrac{1}{1 + \cfrac{1}{1 + \cfrac{1}{1 + \cfrac{1}{1+}}}} \cdots = 1.618\ldots$$

and after a few iterations we find the golden ratio appears again (Table 15-6).

Table 15-6 Golden ratio estimation by continued fractions

1.0000	=1
1.5000	=1+1/(1+1)
1.6667	=1+1/(1+1/(1+1))
1.6000	=1+1/(1+1/(1+1/(1+1)))
1.6250	=1+1/(1+1/(1+1/(1+1/(1+1))))
1.6154	=1+1/(1+1/(1+1/(1+1/(1+1/(1+1)))))
1.6190	=1+1/(1+1/(1+1/(1+1/(1+1/(1+1/(1+1))))))
1.6176	=1+1/(1+1/(1+1/(1+1/(1+1/(1+1/(1+1/(1+1)))))))
1.6182	=1+1/(1+1/(1+1/(1+1/(1+1/(1+1/(1+1/(1+1/(1+1))))))))

15.4 Table of some interesting numbers and constants

Number or approximate value	Name or source	History and properties
0	zero, nought, false	Introduced surprising late in the development of numeracy and mathematics, 0 has the key properties that any value $x+0=x$ and $x*0=0$. Frequently 0 is used in logical operations as the numerical value taken to mean false, but –1 also is used in this connection
0.69314718...	Doubling constant	This value is $\log_e(2)$, and in connection with the doubling interval in geometric series is often approximated to 0.7 or after multiplying by 10, as 7 ("rule of 7")
1	one, unity, true, Fib(1), Fib(2)	One has the key properties that for any x, $1*x=x$
1.20206...	Apery's constant	Zeta(3) or $\zeta(3)=\Sigma 1/k^3$, for $k=1,2...\infty$. This constant, studied by Euler, was recently proven to be Irrational by Apery, but little is otherwise known about it.
1.414...	$\sqrt{2}$	Perhaps the first number proven to be Irrational
1.50659...	Mandelbrot area	The estimated area enclosed by the Mandelbrot set
1.61803...	Golden ratio	$$\frac{1+\sqrt{5}}{2}$$
2	Fib(3); Pri(1)	10 in binary; 2^1
4		100 in binary; 2+2 and 2^2 give us 4, and this is the only Integer with this property
5	Fib(5); Pri(3)	Used as a number (counting) base in a few societies (one hand); all numbers multiplied by 5 end in either 0 or 5, hence such numbers cannot be primes. By exclusion, all primes must end in either 1,3,7 or 9. There are only 5 regular or *Platonic* solids in 3 dimensions: tetrahedron (4 faces, each a triangle); cube (6 faces, all squares); octahedron (8 faces, all triangles); dodecahedron (12 faces, all pentagons); and icosahedron (20 faces, all triangles)
6	Perfect(1), Small World/Degrees of Separation	1+2+3=6 so 6 is a Perfect number; and 1*2*3=3! =6. 6 is also the number associated with the notion of a 'small world' and '6 degrees of separation'. This suggests that if you count your immediate friends and family as 1 step away from you, and their immediate friends and family as 2-steps away from you, then within 6 steps you will have an indirect association with every person in the world ("it's a small world"). The mathematician Erdös is responsible for a variation on this idea that is now known as an Erdös number. Anyone who co-authored a published paper with Erdös has an Erdös number of 1 (there are 502 of these), whilst anyone who has co-authored a paper with someone with an Erdös number of 1 has an Erdös number of 2, and so forth. At present over 300,000 mathematicians have a recorded number. Following the small worlds rule, within 6 steps one might expect every living mathematician in the world who has co-authored papers at the time to have an Erdös number of 6 or less. Authors with an Erdös number of 1 who co-authored more than one paper with Erdös are now

Number or approximate value	Name or source	History and properties
		given fractional values, the smallest of which is 1/62. For more details about these ideas see the Erdös Number Project at: http://www.oakland.edu/enp/ . 6 is the kissing number in 2D
7	Week; Shuffle; Mer$_3$; Prime(4)	Days in week; Shuffle: If a deck of 52 cards is 'riffle shuffled' the arrangement of cards is not truly random until 7 shuffles have been made (the result of research conducted in 1990); 7 is the number of colours required to completely colour a map on a one-fold torus
8	Fib(6), Byte	1000 in binary; $8=2^3$, thus 8 can be generated as a prime number (2) raised to a prime power (3). The same is true for 9 (below) and the pair 8 and 9 are the only sequential numbers with this property
9		$9=3^2$; 9 has the unusual property that any Integer that is divisible by 9 can be identified by adding up its digits until either the number 9 is left, or another number is found. For example, is the number 10893 divisible by 9? We compute 1+0+8+9+3=21 and then 2+1=3, which is not 9, so the answer is No. Clearly every re-arrangement of the digits in 10893 will have the same result, whereas 10593 and every combination of these digits is divisible by 9.
11	repunit; Prime(5)	The term repunit is short for repeated unit, so 11, 111, 1111 etc. are all repunit numbers. If we write R_n for the repunit with n decimal digits, then R_2, R_{19}, R_{27} and R_{317} are all known to be prime. 11 is the currently suggested number of dimensions of the universe. 7 of these dimensions are regarded as being infinitesimally small and folded in upon themselves, the remainder being the 3 conventional dimensions of space plus the dimension of time.
12	Dozen, kissing number	The base of the duodecimal system, widely used as it combines the benefits of the base60 systems with the base10 systems (60=12*5 and 6*10), and is convenient for simple fractions, ½, ¼, 1/3 etc. Used in English currency (12p=1 shilling) pre-decimalisation, and retained for inches in one foot. The Duodecimal Society (est. 1944) proposed using X for 10 and E for eleven, to extend the digits for a base12 system). 12 is the kissing number in 3D
13	Fib(7), Prime(6)	Often regarded as unlucky (possibly related to the Last Supper), many US streets have no number 13 and tall buildings have no 13th floor (at least, no floor named the 13th). 13 (treize in French) is the number of cards in a suit (see also, e) and the number of weeks in a quarter year. 13^2 is the sum of 5^2+12^2 and thus the hypotenuse in the second set of Pythagorean triples, (5,12,13). A 'baker's dozen' i.e. 12+ 1 for good luck
16		10000 in binary; $16=2^4$
20	Score	Used in a variety of contexts, including the Biblical 'score', and in several number systems, including English pre-decimalisation currency (20 shillings)
21	Fib(8)	21=1+2+3+4+5+6= the numbers or pips on six-sided dice

Number or approximate value	Name or source	History and properties
24		$1*2*3*4=4!$
26		Sacred to the Jewish faith, the number 26 is produced when the Hebrew for God, YAHWEH or YHWH, written as יהוה in Hebrew, are treated as decimal numbers and summed. YHWH equates to the numbers, i.e. positions, in the Hebrew alphabet 5,6,10,5
32		100000 in binary; $32=2^5$
42	Life, the Universe and Everything!	101010 in binary ; "You're really not going to like it," observed Deep Thought. "Tell us!" All right," said Deep Thought. "The Answer to the Great Question..." "Yes...!" "Of Life, the Universe, and Everything..." said Deep Thought. "Yes...!" "Is..." said Deep Thought, and paused. "Yes...!" "Is..." "Yes...!!!...?" "Forty-two," said Deep Thought, with infinite majesty and calm. From "The Hitchhiker's Guide to the Galaxy", by Douglas Adams
55	Fib(10)	$55 = 1+2+3+4+5+6+7+8+9+10$ $55 = 1^2+2^2+3^2+4^2+5^2$
60		Base of the sexigesimal system, with units of 1, 60, 3600 etc.; basis of time in minutes in one hour and seconds in one minute; and of angles measured in whole seconds (60 seconds in one degree) and degrees in a circle ($6*60=360$ degrees)
64		$64=2^6$
70		$70^2=1^2+2^2+3^2+4^2+5^2 ...+24^2$; this is the only sequence which exhibits this property; the Biblical age of man (three score and 10)
89	Fib(11), Prime(24)	
91	Taxicab(with negatives)	The smallest number that can be represented as the sum of two positive or negative cubes in two different ways: 3^3+4^3 and -5^3+6^3.
128		$128=2^7$
144	Fib(12), a gross	12^2 (=100 in base12)
256		$256=2^8$
360		Degrees in a circle (see 60); days in a Babylonian year
666	Number of the beast (the Bible, Revelations Ch13, verse 18)	In Roman numerals DCLXVI=666 , i.e. using each numeral once and in order. This may be the (coded) origin of this number, but this is pure speculation. Inevitably there has been much investigation of this number and many curious relationships identified, none of which appear to have any particular significance!
1024	kilobyte	2^{10}, kbyte
1089	Eye-spy (cited by Acheson)	This number is always found as the result of the following simple operation: take any 3 digit number, e.g. 234, reverse the sequence of digits, 432 and subtract the smaller number, 432-234=198. Now reverse this new 3 digit number and add it to the value we have just found, thus 198+891=1089. 1089*9=9801, the number reversed, and the fraction 11/101= the repeating decimal 0.10891089...
1729	Taxicab(Ramanujan)	The smallest number that can be represented as the

Number or approximate value	Name or source	History and properties
		sum of two positive cubes in two different ways: 12^3+1^3 and 10^3+9^3. This was the number of the Taxi that the English mathematician Hardy stated that he took when visiting Ramanujan in Putney
5050	Gauss	$5050=1+2+3+4...+99+100$; more generally, the sum of the first n digits is $n(n+1)/2$, reputedly noticed by Gauss when aged 10
6174	Kaprekar constant	Take any 4 digit number, whose digits are not all the same, e.g. 1729. Arrange the digits in descending order and subtract the reverse: 9721-1279 =8442; repeat this process, so we have 8442-2448=5994, and 9954-4599=5355, 5553-3555=1998, 9981-1899=8082, 8820-0288=8532, 8532-2358=6174. This value is the end of the sequence, and every sequence ends this way! The Kaprekar process, which was discovered by D R Kaprekar in 1949, can be applied for different numbers of digits.
10,000	myriad	from the Greek, also meaning countless
32,767		$2^{16}-1$, the largest Integer storable in one word of a 16-bit computer or digital device
1,000,000	Million	10^6, mega, M
1,048,576	Megabyte	2^{20}, Mbyte or Mb
16,777,216	Truecolour	2^{24}, the number of colours determined by storing 1 byte for each of three distinct colour components, Red, Blue and Green (hence '24bit colour')
635,318,657	Taxicab 4th power (Euler)	The smallest number that can be represented as the sum of two fourth powers in two different ways: 133^4+134^4 and 158^4+59^4
1,000,000,000	Billion	10^9, giga, G, North American billion, a term now widely used internationally (cf Trillion)
1,073,741,824	Gigabyte	2^{30}; Now widely used, especially in data storage connections, as in gigabytes of disk
4,294,967,295		$2^{32}-1$, the largest Integer storable in one word of a 32-bit computer or digital device
10^{12}	Trillion	10^6*10^6, tera, T, a billion in Europe/less commonly used now; Terabyte storage devices are now widely available (2^{40} bytes)
10^{15}	Quadrillion (peta, P)	Binary version =2^{50} bytes
10^{100}	A 'googol'	1 with 100 zeros after it (not to be confused with the search engine, Google
$2^{24036583}-1$	Mer$_{41}$	The 41st Mersenne Prime, the second largest prime number known at the time of writing, discovered in 2003. This number has over 7 million digits
$2^{25964951}-1$	Mer$_{42}$	The 42nd Mersenne Prime, the largest prime number known at the time of writing, discovered in 2005. This number has almost 8 million digits

16 SEQUENCES

16.1 Identifying sequences

As we saw in the discussion on interesting numbers, many arise from sequences or series of numbers. In general such sequences are infinite sets, generated by some simple rule or pattern. Probably the most important Integer sequence is the set of all prime numbers.

A searchable list of some 100,000 interesting Integer sequences is maintained by AT&T and is accessible via a web site at:

  http://www.research.att.com/~njas/sequences/

16.2 Table of some interesting Integer sequences

Name	Sequence	History and properties
Fibonacci, Fib(n)	1, 1, 2, 3, 5, 8,13, 21, 34 ...	Fib(n+2)=Fib(n+1)+Fib(n) where Fib(1)=Fib(2)=1
Perfect, Per(n)	6, 28, 496, 8128...	Perfect numbers are those whose factors add up to the number, e.g. 6=1+2+3 ; for all even Perfect numbers $Per(n)=2^n(2^{n+1}-1)$ where $(2^{n+1}-1)$ is a Mersenne Prime (see below), thus $Per(1)=2(2^2-1)=6$ and $Per(1)=2^2(2^3-1)=28$
Prime	2, 3, 5, 7, 11, 13, 17, 19, 23, 29...	These are Integers that are only divisible by themselves and 1; all other Integers >1 are called Composite
Pythagorean triples	{3,4,5}, {5,12,13}, {20,21,29}	Integer triples {a,b,c} that satisfy the equation $a^2+b^2=c^2$; there are an infinite number of such triples. All Pythagorean triples can be generated using an algorithm devised by Diophantus of Alexandria dating back to c.250AD. This states that if p and q are any two numbers, such that (a) one is even and one is odd, (b) p>q, and (iii) they share no common divisors other than 1, then the set $\{2pq, p^2-q^2, p^2+q^2\}$ and any Integer multiple of the set, will be a Pythagorean triple. For example, let p=4, q=1 then we have {8,15,17}.
Mersenne numbers, Mer(n)	1, 3, 7, 15, 31, 63, 127, 255, 511, 1023, ...	$Mer(n)=2^n-1$ (compare to Mersenne primes, below)
Mersenne primes, Mer(p)	3, 7, 31, 127, 8191,13107...	Mer(p) is of the form 2^p-1 (compare to Fermat primes, below), but only for selected values of p; Mer_k denotes the kth Mersenne prime
Fibonacci primes, Fib(p)	2, 3, 5,13, 89, 233, 1597, ...	Fib(p)=prime if p=prime, except for Fib(4)=3
Factorials	1, 2, 6, 24, 120, 720, 5040,40320...	written as n!, this is the product of the first n Integers, i.e. 1*2*3*...*n
Fermat primes, Fer(p)	5,17, 257, 65537, 4294967297 ...	$Fer(p)=2^p+1$, where p is itself a power of 2, i.e. $p=2^n$, giving 2, 4, 8, 16, 32 ...; Fermat postulated that all numbers of this type are primes, but in fact the last number in this sequence is not prime, and no others have been identified. The last number in the sequence shown has factors (is divisible by) 641 and 6700417
Newton or Kissing numbers	2, 6, 12, 24, 40, 72, 126, 272...	The maximum number of identically sized 'spheres' in n dimensions (n=1,2,3,4 ...) that can just touch or 'kiss' a central sphere. A 1-dimensional 'sphere' is simply a line, so it can be touched by 2 others, whilst on a plane, 6 circles of the same size (2-d spheres) is the maximum. The arrangement is such that one sphere is located centrally, with a further 12 spheres touching it and each other surrounding this central sphere. This is not the same as the most dense packing of spheres in 3D (e.g. packing oranges into a very large box). In the case of packing, spheres arranged on either a regular square or hexagonal lattice pattern will pack as layers in 3D and occupy roughly 75% of the available space. The kissing number sequence is known for n=1 to 9, and 24. For other dimensions lower bounds are known (e.g. it is known that at least 336 10-dimensional spheres can kiss).

APPENDIX 1: MATHEMATICAL EXTRAS

This Appendix includes brief details on a number of items raised in the text, which involve a little more mathematical detail. In each case a basic explanation is provided and readers should refer to more thorough descriptions and discussions in the various books and web sites referred to in Appendix II.

Balloon volume

In calculating the volume of Larry's balloons I have assumed that they were perfectly spherical since this is a reasonably good approximation for weather balloons. Assuming we do not know the formula for the volume of a sphere, radius r, we can approximate it or deduce it in much the same way as we calculated the area of a circle. First, image the sphere, radius r, as being a ball inside a box. Each edge of the box would be 2r in length, so the volume of the box would be 2r x 2r x 2r = $8r^3$. Now the sphere is going to have a volume less than that of the box, so will be of the form Ar^3 where A<<8. The symbol << here means 'quite a bit less than'.

Now a sphere can be thought of as a stack of very thin circles, like CDs or vinyl records or slices through an apple, each one slightly smaller than the previous until at the top and bottom (North and South poles) the disks are vanishingly small. If we could calculate the volume of each disk and add these up, we would have an approximation to the total volume for a sphere. We already know

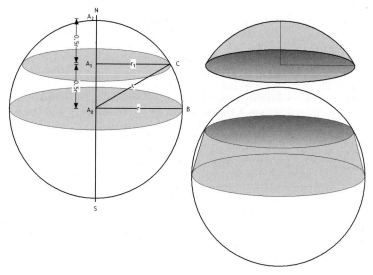

Figure A1 Balloon volume

that each disk has an area of πr^2, and that the formula for the volume of a sphere is going to be something like Ar^3, so we expect the formula for volume will be of the form $k\pi r^3$. Since we have already deduced that $A=k\pi<<8$ we now know that $k<<8/\pi$, so k is probably less than 2.

Suppose now we separate the sphere very crudely into thick slices or disks. We can imagine dividing the upper half of the sphere into two parts with a horizontal slice half way from its centre line or equator (see the diagram on page 181). The area of our slice through the sphere at A_0 will be πr^2 and at A_1 will be πr_1^2. Using this information we can approximate the volume of the first thick slice lying between A_0 and A_1 as the average of the area at A_0 and A_1 times the thickness of the slice, which is $r/2$, so the volume of this slice is roughly $r/2(\pi r_1^2+\pi r^2)/2$, or $\pi r(r_1^2+r^2)/4$. The slice from A_1 to A_2 is calculated in the same way, but is simpler because at A_2 the radius is 0, so the estimated volume of this slice is simply $\pi r(r_1^2+0)/4$.

For the whole sphere we now add these two slices together and double the result to include the lower half, giving a final result $V\approx 2r(\pi(r_1^2+r^2)/4+\pi r_1^2/4)$ i.e. $V\approx\pi r(r_1^2+r^2/2)$.

We will have the final answer if we know r_1. We can obtain this using the triangle A_0A_1C and the well known Pythagoras relationship $r^2=r_1^2+(r/2)^2$ giving $r_1^2=3r^2/4$. We now have $V\approx\pi r(3r^2/4+r^2/2)=5\pi r^3/4$ as a first estimate, i.e. k is approximately $5/4$. From the diagram of the approximation used for the first slice we can see that this is an underestimate. If we repeat this process, taking thinner and thinner slices, we obtain a better and better approximation and will find that k tends to a fixed value $k=4/3$. So a balloon of radius 4 foot will have a volume $V= 4\pi r^3/3$ cubic feet, or 268.08... cubic feet. The convergence to this result is fast — with only 8 slices of one hemisphere $k=1.333125$, very close to $4/3$.

Standard deviation

The term standard deviation has been used on a number of occasions in this book, and it is useful to provide details on how it is calculated. It provides a measure of the average difference of a set of data values from their overall mean, but because differences are positive and negative, we need to make special provisions if an average measure of these differences is to be obtained. The first things we will do is define our data values as a set of n items, $\{x_i, i=1,2...n\}$. The average of these items is their total divided by n, or

$$\bar{x} = \frac{\sum_{i=1}^{n} x_i}{n}$$

where the symbol x with a bar over it is used to represent the average over all the x values (this line symbol is known as a macron). Suppose the values were 2,12,0.5,19 and 178, then the average of these 5 values would be $211.5/5=42.3$ — if you wish, you can enter these values into

Excel and then use the average() function to obtain this answer. If you now calculate the difference of each value from the mean (the deviations) and add these up you will find the answer totals 0 — this is feature of the mean. If we want a measure of average differences we need to get rid of the negative signs, either by ignoring them (taking the absolute value, implemented in Excel as abs()), or by taking the square of each number, averaging the sum of squares, and then taking the square root to get back to the same basic scale.

These operations are illustrated in the table below. First we have the x values, with the total and the average computed in Excel as =AVERAGE(B2:B6) or as =SUM(B2:B6)/5. Next is a column of deviations, which can be seen sum to 0. Then a column of absolute deviations is shown and the average of these is 54.28. Finally the squared deviations approach is illustrated, with an average that is huge, but once we take the square root, we get 68.18622, which is the *standard deviation*. You will also see that the same value is repeated on the line below — in this case the Excel function STDEVP(B2:B6) has been applied (the *population* standard deviation — see below).

x	Deviations	Abs(Devs)	Dev^2		
2	-40.3	40.3	1624.09		
12	-30.3	30.3	918.09		
0.5	-41.8	41.8	1747.24		
19	-23.3	23.3	542.89		
178	135.7	135.7	18414.49		
Totals	0	271.4	23246.8		
Averages 42.3		54.28	4649.36	68.18622	
				68.18622	STDEVP
				76.23451	STDEV

Finally, a slightly larger result is shown generated from the function STDEV(B2:B6). This is an adjusted value, based on the assumption that the 5 *x*-values we have are actually random samples from a much larger set of values (or true *population* of all values). If we had this much larger set we could be confident that the average spread of values would actually be greater, and this will generally be by a factor of *n*/(*n*-1) times the sum of squares value, so 5/4 in our case, which after allowing for the square root process brings the *sample* standard deviation up to 76.23451.

Solution to rounding error equation

The expression we wish to evaluate is:

$$x = \frac{1335}{4}b^6 + a^2\left(11a^2b^2 - b^6 - 121b^4 - 2\right) + \frac{11}{2}b^8 + \frac{a}{2b}$$, with a =77617 and b=33096.

We can separate this calculation into a series of four smaller problems:

$x = x1 + x2 + x3 + x4$, where

$$x1 = \frac{1335}{4}b^6, x2 = a^2\left(11a^2b^2 - b^6 - 121b^4 - 2\right)x3 = \frac{11}{2}b^8, x4 = \frac{a}{2b}$$

When we calculate the four separate parts of the original expression we find:

$x1$ (29 digits) $=0.43860575084639316193070383104 \times 10^{30}$
$x2$ (36 digits) $=-0.791711177927471220749429663222877389 \times 10^{37}$
$x3$ (37 digits) $=+0.7917111340668961361101134701524942848 \times 10^{37}$
$x4 =1.172603940...$

The values shown in bold highlight the reason for this calculation being more complicated than appears at first sight — the first 7 digits of x2 and x3 are identical, and they are the same order of magnitude (E+37). If we add x2 and x3 we get

$x2+x3=-0.4386057508463931619307038310_{42} \times 10^{30}$

which is identical to x1 but with a negative sign and one additional digit, 2, thus x1+x2+x3=-2. Finally, when we add x4 we get the answer -0.82739...

Rates of change, differentiation and integration

Gravitational acceleration
In our discussion of gravitational acceleration we found that the distance you fall is related to how long it is since you stepped out of the helicopter, i.e. how much time has elapsed. The formula we came up with was of the form $z=at^2+bt$, where a and b were constants. We showed that a constant rate of acceleration gave rise to this result and that this bore some relation to the field of mathematics known as *calculus*. To explain this relation a bit more thoroughly I am going to carry out the numerical process in reverse, using Δt to indicate a very small interval of time, in fact an interval so small that $(\Delta t)^2$ is vanishingly small.

I start with the equation we derived, $z=at^2+bt$, which identified how many metres we had fallen at time t. Now at time $T=t+\Delta t$ we will have fallen a bit further: to say $z^*=aT^2+bT$ metres. So, in the tiny interval of time, Δt, we have fallen z*-z metres, i.e. (z*-z) metres per Δt time, or (z*-z)/Δt since *per* is equivalent to 'divide by'. This gives us our *rate* of fall, and we can expand (z*-z)/Δt by substituting in the expressions for z and z* to see what its value might be, as follows:

$y=(z^*-z)/\Delta t=[a(t+\Delta t)^2+b(t+\Delta t)-(at^2+bt)]/\Delta t;$

Now multiply out the first term in brackets (the one that is squared) to give

$y=[at^2+2at\Delta t+a(\Delta t)^2+bt+b\Delta t-at^2-bt)]/\Delta t;$

Several parts now cancel each other out, and we can ignore the term $a(\Delta t)^2$ because it is very small indeed, giving us

$y=[+2at\Delta t+b\Delta t)]/\Delta t;$

And finally, cancelling out the Δt's we get

$y=2at+b$

We use the notation dz/dt for this expression and call it the *differential of z with respect to t*. The reverse process we call the integral of z with respect to t and often use an extended S (for summation), $\int$, to indicate this operation. You can follow the same procedure for expressions containing higher powers of t such as $z=t^3$ (t or x etc., these letters are just used to indicate a variable). If you try this yourself you will quickly discover the general rule that if $z=t^n$ then $dz/dt=nt^{n-1}$. The reverse process means that if $y=t^n$ then $z=\int y dt=t^{n+1}/(n+1)$ (possibly plus a constant) — if you are not sure how I got this answer try differentiating t^{n+1} using our general rule and see what you get.

You can carry out all of these operations directly using Maple's integration function, int(,) which should not be confused with the widespread use in software packages and languages of int() to mean the Integer part, and Maple's differentiation function diff(,) as follows (results are shown in bold):

z:=a*t^2+b*t; **at²+bt**
R1 := diff(z,t); **2at+b** (note, this function means differentiate z with respect to t)
R2 := int(R1,t); **at²+bt** (note, this function means integrate R1 with respect to t)

These examples show simple differentiation, and what is known as *indefinite* integration — the term indefinite refers to the fact that we have not specified any limits on the values that time t can take and so the result we are given is shown in symbolic, or equation form. If we specify values for t=start and t=end then we obtain a *definite* integral. For example, with a=9.81m/s² as the gravitational acceleration and b=0 as the initial rate of fall, we can evaluate the definite integral from t=0 until we hit the ground 1000 metres below just n seconds later. This can be achieved using Maple to estimate the total time required by varying the upper time value, n, e.g.

z:=9.81*t; n:=14.279;
int(z,t=0..n); **1000.08**

The result n=14.279 seconds confirms the results we obtained in Section 3.5 by two different means, one numerical/graphical and the other utilising the solution equation.

Population growth and exponential rates of change
We can also apply these methods to other functions that we have discussed elsewhere in this book, such as the exponential function, e^t, or the trig functions, sin(t) and cos(t). I will do the

same calculations for e^t to clarify this process, and leave you to try it for $sin(x)$ — in the latter case you will need to know that $sin(x+y)=sin(x)cos(y)+cos(x)sin(y)$, and remember that $cos(0)=1$ and $sin(0)=0$. You should find that the differential of $sin(x)$ is $cos(x)$, and for $cos(x)$ you should get $-sin(x)$. Thus the integral of $sin(x)=-cos(x)$ and the integral of $cos(x)$ is $sin(x)$.

To obtain the differential of $z=e^t$ we proceed exactly as before, writing:

$$y=(z^*-z)/\Delta t=(e^{t+\Delta t}-e^t)/\Delta t$$

Now from our knowledge of exponents we can write this as:

$$y=(e^t e^{\Delta t}-e^t)/\Delta t$$

and then move the common part, e^t, outside the brackets:

$$y=e^t(e^{\Delta t}-1)/\Delta t$$

The tricky question is "what happens to $(e^{\Delta t}-1)/\Delta t$ when Δt becomes very small?". We could test this numerically, using Excel for example, but it might be a bit risky. This is because dividing by a very small number can quickly result in computer errors — in fact Excel starts to fail if Δt is 0.00000001 or smaller, as the following data shows (the Excel formulas are of the form =(EXP(B1)-1)/B1):

$(e^{\Delta t}-1)/\Delta t$	Δt
1.051709180756480	0.1
1.005016708416790	0.01
1.000500166708380	0.001
1.000050001667140	0.0001
1.000005000006960	0.00001
1.000000499962180	0.000001
1.000000049433680	0.0000001
0.999999993922529	0.00000001
1.000000082740370	0.000000001
1.000000082740370	0.0000000001
1.000000082740370	0.00000000001
1.000088900582340	0.000000000001
0.999200722162641	0.0000000000001
0.999200722162641	0.00000000000001
1.110223024625160	0.000000000000001

A better approach is to recognise that we can use the series expansion for e^x that we saw in Section 15.2 where $x=\Delta t$ in this case:

$$e^{\Delta t} = 1+\frac{\Delta t^1}{1}+\frac{\Delta t^2}{2.1}+\frac{\Delta t^3}{3.2.1}+\frac{\Delta t^4}{4.3.2.1}+... \approx 1+\Delta t$$

if we drop terms in Δt^2 and higher, so we see that as Δt tends to 0 (we sometimes use the symbol

→ to mean 'tends to'):

[$e^{\Delta t}$ -1]/Δt→1, as Δt→0, so we find the surprising result
$y=e^t$

So the differential of $z=e^t$ is $dz/dt=e^t$ and by implication, the integral $\int e^t dt=e^t$ also. This demonstrates another remarkable, important and unique property of e. If we had tried this process with 10^t, say, we would have found the differential was $10^t \log_e(10)$, because $10^t=\log_e(10)*e^t$. As before, we can confirm these operations using Maple:

z:=diff(10^t,t); **$10^t \ln(10)$**
z:=int(10^t,t); **$10^t/\ln(10)$**

Mercator's map

In this final subsection we will use a little more mathematics to obtain the rules for creating a Mercator Projection map. The separation of the lines of latitude in Mercator's map was stated in Section 12.2.2 to be:

$$\frac{1}{2}\log\frac{(1+x)}{(1-x)} = \frac{1}{2}\log(1+x) - \frac{1}{2}\log(1-x) = x + \frac{x^3}{3} + \frac{x^5}{5} + \frac{x^7}{7} + \dots$$

where x=sin(latitude). It was also stated, without much justification other than numerical calculations, that this was the result obtained from adding up (integrating) $1/\cos(\theta)$, where θ represents latitude, for sufficiently tiny increments of latitude, $d\theta$. So we need to find:

$$\int\frac{1}{\cos(\theta)}d\theta$$

If we multiply the top and bottom of this expression by $\cos(\theta)$ we get

$$\int\frac{\cos(\theta)}{\cos^2(\theta)}d\theta = \int\frac{\cos(\theta)}{1-\sin^2(\theta)}d\theta$$

Now let x=sin(θ). We then have $dx/d\theta=\cos(\theta)$ and thus $dx=\cos(\theta)d\theta$, and so

$$\int\frac{\cos(\theta)}{1-\sin^2(\theta)}d\theta = \int\frac{1}{1-x^2}dx$$

Now $(1-x^2)=(1-x)(1+x)$ and this in turn equals

$$\frac{1}{2}\left(\frac{1}{1-x} + \frac{1}{1+x}\right)$$

So the two integrals we need are

$$\frac{1}{2}\int\frac{1}{1-x}dx + \frac{1}{2}\int\frac{1}{1+x}dx$$

This is beginning to look like parts of the expression we started with. To evaluate the two integrals it is simplest to start with the proposed answers and see what rate of change is associated with these expressions, as we did in the previous subsections of this Appendix. We can limit our discussion to one of these, $\frac{1}{2}\log(1+x)$, since $\frac{1}{2}\log(1-x)$ follows exactly the same pattern. If we look at the rate of change of $\log(1+x)$ we need to evaluate

$$[\log(1+x+\Delta x)-\log(1+x)]/\Delta x \text{ as } \Delta x\to 0.$$

We can use Nicholas Mercator's series for $\log(1+x)$ to do this, and we obtain:

(A) $\quad \log(1+x+\Delta x) = x + \Delta x - \dfrac{(x+\Delta x)^2}{2} + \dfrac{(x+\Delta x)^3}{3} - \dfrac{(x+\Delta x)^4}{4} + \ldots \quad$, and

(B) $\quad \log(1+x) = x - \dfrac{x^2}{2} + \dfrac{x^3}{3} - \dfrac{x^4}{4} + \ldots$

If we expand the bracketed terms in the right hand side of (A) and drop all terms in $(\Delta x)^2$ and higher powers (as these will rapidly tend to 0 as $\Delta x\to 0$), we have:

(A1) $\quad \log(1+x+\Delta x) \approx (x+\Delta x) - (\dfrac{x^2}{2} + x.\Delta x) + (\dfrac{x^3}{3} + x^2.\Delta x) - (\dfrac{x^4}{4} + x^3.\Delta x) + \ldots$

We can now subtract (B) from (A1). Most of the terms drop out and we are left with:

(A1)-(B)$= \Delta x - x.\Delta x + x^2.\Delta x - x^3.\Delta x + \ldots$

Finally we divide through by Δx to obtain the rate of change or differential of $\log(1+x)$:

$1 - x + x^2 - x^3 + x^4\ldots$

This result does not look much like the expression in our integral, $1/(1+x)$. However, in order to show these are actually the same expressions we need to expand $(1+x)^n$, which we came across in our discussion of exponentials. This is called the binomial expansion, and we can show that

$(1+x)^n=1+nx+ n(n-1)x^2/2!+n(n-1)(n-2)x^3/3!+\ldots$

In our case, if we take $n=-1$ we have

$1/(1+x)=(1+x)^{-1}=1-x+x^2-x^3+\ldots$

which is the series above. So, eventually we have arrived at the result:

$$\int \frac{1}{1+x}dx = \log(1+x)$$

and if we go through the same process for $\log(1-x)$ we will find:

$$\int \frac{1}{1-x}dx = -\log(1-x)$$

Now, using our earlier results, we have

$$\int \frac{1}{\cos(\theta))} d\theta = \frac{1}{2}\int \frac{1}{1+x} dx + \frac{1}{2}\int \frac{1}{1-x} dx = \frac{1}{2}\log(1+x) - \frac{1}{2}\log(1-x)$$

which, fortunately, is the final result we expected!

This entire procedure has used the equator as the starting point and integrated in a direction due North or South to obtain Mercator's map. The map is very accurate in terms of shapes and sizes near to the equator, but not elsewhere, and is correct in terms of directions everywhere. Most individual countries, such as the UK, do not have a very large East-West extent, so a clever trick is to turn the Mercator Projection through 90 degrees and treat a line of longitude, e.g. the Greenwich Meridian, 0°, as the starting point and generate a Mercator map in the same manner as before but this time extending a few degrees East and West instead of North and South (the scale of the map remains correct to within 1% over a range of 10 degrees). The result is called a Transverse Mercator map. As I mentioned in the text, projections based on this idea are used for many national and regional mapping systems, including: those of the UK (GB National Grid, with central meridian at 2°W, passing N-S roughly through Bristol); much of the USA (e.g. the State Plane Coordinate System); but not normally for regions that have a large East-West extent, such as the former USSR or the US states of Tenessee or Kentucky.

APPENDIX 2: RESOURCES

Books and articles

The following is a selection of books, most of which are highly readable, but a number of which require a reasonable level of mathematical knowledge. Books marked with an asterisk (*) are suitable for those with a good basic understanding of mathematics, often including some calculus. As far as possible recently published works have been included, as these should be easier to obtain from bookshops or Internet retailers.

Abbott E A (1885) *Flatland: A romance of many dimensions*, subtitled "by 'A Square', with illustrations by the author", Roberts Brothers, Boston. An extract of this work, with commentary, is included in J R Newman's collection (cited below). Recent reprints are available from Dover Publications, Penguin Books and others

Acheson D (2002) *1089 and all that*, Oxford University Press, Oxford, UK. A delightful little introduction to mathematics, perhaps the best of its kind in recent years

Adler K (2002) *The measure of all things*, Little Brown (Time Warner), London. A detailed account of the measurement exercise that led to the definition of a metre and the subsequent metrification programme

Apostol T M (1974*) *Mathematical Analysis*, 2nd Ed., Addison-Wesley, Mass, USA. A thorough introduction to formal mathematical analysis

Conte S D, de Boor C (1965*) *Elementary numerical analysis*, McGraw-Hill Kogakusha, Tokyo. A well-written book providing explanations of a wide range of methods, with emphasis on convergence and error analysis

Berlinghoff W P, Gouvea F Q (2004) *Math through the ages*, Oxton House Publishers, Farmington, ME, USA; Described by its authors as "A gentle history for teachers and others", this excellent new book provides a highly accessible compact guide to the history and practice of mathematics, combined with educational references and projects

Dunham W (1999*) *Euler, the master of us all*, The Mathematical Association of America, Washington DC. A highly readable book describing a small but fascinating selection of Euler's results

Farmalo G (ed) (2002) *It must be beautiful*, subtitled "Great equations of modern times", Granta Books, London. Some chapters of this book are more challenging for non-physicists. It includes a chapter by Robert May on the Logistic Map

Flegg H G (1974) *From geometry to topology*, English Universities Press, reprinted by Dover Publications in 2001. This highly approachable book has very clear explanations and diagrams. It was used as part of the Open University's course materials, with lectures delivered by Flegg, and was highly praised at the time. The original printing predates the solution of the 4-colour problem

Gonzales R C, Woods R E (2002*) *Digital image processing*, 2nd ed., Prentice Hall, New Jersey. The classic 'academic' text on digital image processing — highly readable but not for the faint hearted!

Hobgen L (1993) *Mathematics for the million*, W W Norton, New York. Sub-titled "How to master the magic of numbers" this book was originally written in 1937 and updated by Hobgen some 30 years later. A classic work, it covers the full sweep of mathematics to basic calculus and statistics, without presuming too much of the reader apart from considerable patience and determination. Praised by Einstein and H G Wells amongst others, it was reprinted in paperback in 1993

Hoffman P (1998) *The man who loved only numbers*, subtitled "The story of Paul Erdös and the search for mathematical truth", Fourth Estate, London. A highly readable and largely non-mathematical biography of the most prolific and perhaps most eccentric mathematician of recent times. Erdös published more works than any other mathematician in history except for Euler

Hua L-K (1982*) *Introduction to number theory*, Springer-Verlag, Berlin, translated from the Chinese (1952) original by Peter Shiu, with updates in 1981 for the new edition. A demanding work which covers the fundamental theorems and proofs of number theory

Ifrah G (1998) *The universal history of numbers*, Translated from the French, The Harvill Press, London. An encyclopaedic work, full of fascinating diagrams of number systems and methods of counting through the ages, including evidence from pre-history, the number systems of the Egyptians, Sumerians and Hittites, the Chinese and Japanese traditions, Greek and Roman developments, and the Indo-Arabic legacy

Klein M (1990*) *Mathematical thought from ancient to modern times*, Oxford University Press, Oxford, UK. The most complete and authoritative single-volume survey of the vast subject, written with great clarity and remarkably well structured

Körner T W (1996) *The pleasure of counting*, Cambridge University Press, Cambridge, UK. A book full of great stories and thought provoking examples of mathematical applications. Designed as an introductory text for those interested in mathematics "from 14 year olds upwards" it is perhaps a little more demanding than its title suggests

Mackay R J, Oldford R W (2002) *Scientific method*, Statistical method and the Speed of Light, Working Paper 2002-02, Dept of Statistics and Actuarial Science, University of Waterloo, Canada. A delightful paper, in the spirit of R A Fisher's "Statistics of a Lady Tasting Tea" (the latter is included in J R Newman's collection, cited below). Provides an insight into Michelson's 1879 experiment and explanation of the role and method of statistics in the larger context of science

Newman J R (1960) *The world of mathematics* (four volumes), subtitled "A small library of the literature of mathematics from A'h-mose the scribe to Albert Einstein, presented with commentaries and notes by J R Newman", George Allen & Unwin, London. A fantastic collection of articles and original papers by almost every mathematician of note from Ancient times up until 1960

Ordnance Survey (2001) *A guide to coordinate systems in Great Britain*, Ordnance Survey

Publications. Obtained from the Ordnance Survey website, www.ordnancesurvey.gov.uk

Press W H, Teukolsky S A, Vettering W T, Flannery B P (1992*) *Numerical recipes in C*, subtitled "The art of scientific computing", 2nd ed., Cambridge University Press, Cambridge, UK. A demanding book, designed principally for software engineers, full of valuable information

Roberts F S, Suppes P (1967) *Some problems in the geometry of visual perception*, Synthese, 17, 173-201. A seminal article on the fundamental nature of human vision

Schneier B (1996*) *Applied Cryptography: Protocols, Algorithms and Source Code in C*, 2nd edition, J Wiley & Sons, New York. One of the most recent and widely regarded works on cryptography

Stewart I (2001) *What shape is a snowflake?*, Weidenfeld & Nicholson, London. A beautifully produced and illustrated discussion of patterns in nature and their relationship to mathematics and the development of mathematical ideas

Szpiro G G (2003) *Kepler's Conjecture*, subtitled "How some of the greatest minds in history helped solve one of the oldest math problems in the world", J Wiley & Sons, New Jersey. A recently published quite detailed account of sphere packing problems, kissing numbers and related topics.

Vivaldi F (2001) *Experimental mathematics with MAPLE*, Chapman and Hall/CRC Mathematics, Boca Raton, USA. A workbook introducing a wide range of mathematical topics with the aid of the Maple software package. Designed as a course for first year undergraduates

Walsh G R (1975*) *Methods of optimisation*, J Wiley, London. This work provides an introduction to many of the techniques employed in optimisation, although it predates the introduction of more computationally intensive methods such as simulated annealing, genetic algorithms, cross entropy search and lattice exploration

Wells D G (1993) *Penguin Dictionary of Curious Geometry/Numbers*, Penguin Press Science Series. An invaluable source of information on results and properties relating to thousands of numbers, especially the positive Integers

Web sites

Maths for the Mystified:
The authors website page for this book and related materials

   http://www.mdesmith.com/

Mathworld:
Perhaps the most complete (broadest) source of regularly updated mathematical information available anywhere (designed for use by mathematicians primarily)

   http://mathworld.wolfram.com/

Mathcentre:
A UK initiative supported by the charity Education Broadcast Services Trust. This web site provides

online resources in the form of PDF documents and videos explaining many areas of mathematics. They aim "to deliver mathematics support materials, free of charge, to students, teachers, lecturers and everyone looking for post-16 maths help"

http://www.mathcentre.ac.uk/

Numbers:
An excellent source of information on a variety of constants, with details of series formulas and much besides

http://numbers.computation.free.fr/Constants/constants.html

History of Mathematics:
Based at St Andrew's University in Scotland, the web site known as MacTutor is perhaps the most extensive (broadest) source of mathematical biographies available. It incorporates linked topic-based historical essays on a wide range of subjects, including Number Theory.

http://www-groups.dcs.st-and.ac.uk/~history/

Inverse Symbolic Calculator (ISC):
A project of the Centre for Experimental and Constructive Mathematics (CECM) at Simon Fraser University, Vancouver, Canada

http://www.cecm.sfu.ca/projects/ISC/ISCmain.html

Integer sequences:
Encyclopaedia of Integer sequences — an AT&T Research project incorporating online search facilities covering around 100,000 known sequences

http://www.research.att.com/~njas/sequences/Seis.html

Fibonacci series
Ron Knott's award winning web site on everything you wanted to know about Fibonacci series and a lot more besides

http://www.mcs.surrey.ac.uk/Personal/R.Knott/Fibonacci/

Fractals (MATLab software and more details):

http://ltcmail.ethz.ch/cavin/fractals.html

Mersenne Primes (Great Internet Mersenne Prime Search, GIMPS)
You can join in the search for the largest prime number by accessing this web site and

downloading the free search software provided. This is how opthalmologist Dr Martin Nowak made his recent discovery

http://www.mersenne.org/prime.htm

Bureau International des Poids et Mesures (BIPM):
(International Bureau of Weights and Measures)

http://www1.bipm.org/en/home/

Ordnance Survey:
Source of information, maps and data for the UK

www.ordnancesurvey.gov.uk

PGP:
International PGP home page

http://www.pgpi.org

Software packages and related tools

Adobe:
www.adobe.com
Acrobat PDF file reader (free); PDF Writer and Distiller products for creating PDF files are part of the main Adobe Acrobat software suite

MAPLE:
http://www.maplesoft.com/
Free lessons and tools covering all of the topics in this book, and much more:
http://www.mapleapps.com/powertools/MathEducation.shtml

MATLab:
http://www.mathworks.com

Mathematika:
http://www.wolfram.com/products/mathematica/index.html

Microsoft:
www.microsoft.com

TeX:
http://www.ams.org/tex/ and http://www.tug.org/

INDEX